W9-ATO-948

AMONG FAMOUS BOOKS

AMONG FAMOUS BOOKS

BY

JOHN KELMAN, D.D.

Essay Index Reprint Series

BOOKS FOR LIBRARIES PRESS
FREEPORT, NEW YORK

First Published 1912
Reprinted 1968

LIBRARY OF CONGRESS CATALOG CARD NUMBER:
68-57326

PRINTED IN THE UNITED STATES OF AMERICA

PREFACE

THE object of the following lectures is twofold. They were delivered in the first place for the purpose of directing the attention of readers to books whose literary charm and spiritual value have made them conspicuous in the vast literature of England. Such a task, however, tends to be so discursive as to lose all unity, depending absolutely upon the taste of the individual, and the chances of his experience in reading.

I have accordingly taken for the general theme of the book that constant struggle between paganism and idealism which is the deepest fact in the life of man, and whose story, told in one form or another, provides the matter of all vital literature. This will serve as a thread to give continuity of thought to the lectures, and it will keep them near to central issues.

Having said so much, it is only necessary to add one word more by way of explanation. In quest of the relations between the spiritual and the material, or (to put it otherwise) of the battle between the flesh and the spirit, we shall dip into three different periods of time: (1) Classical, (2) Sixteenth Century, (3) Modern. Each of these has a character of its own, and the glimpses which we shall have of them ought to be interesting in their own right. But the similarity between the three is more striking than the contrast, for human nature does not greatly change, and its deepest struggles are the same in all generations.

CONTENTS

LECTURE I

LECTURE II

LECTURE III

LECTURE IV

LECTURE V

LECTURE VI

LECTURE VII

LECTURE VIII

LECTURE IX

LECTURE X

LECTURE I

THE GODS OF GREECE

IT has become fashionable to divide the rival tendencies of modern thought into the two classes of Hellenistic and Hebraistic. The division is an arbitrary and somewhat misleading one, which has done less than justice both to the Greek and to the Hebrew genius. It has associated Greece with the idea of lawless and licentious paganism, and Israel with that of a forbidding and joyless austerity. Paganism is an interesting word, whose etymology reminds us of a time when Christianity had won the towns, while the villages still worshipped heathen gods. It is difficult to define the word without imparting into our thought of it the idea of the contrast between Christian dogma and all other religious thought and life. This, however, would be an extemely unfair account of the matter, and, in the present volume, the word will be used without reference either to nationality or to creed, and it will stand for the materialistic and earthly tendency as against spiritual idealism of any kind. Obviously such paganism as this, is not a thing which has died out with the passing of heathen systems of religion. It is terribly alive in the heart of modern England, whether formally believing or unbelieving. Indeed there is the twofold life of puritan and pagan within us all. A recent well-known theologian wrote to his sister: "I am naturally a cannibal, and I find now my true vocation to be in the South Sea Islands, not after your plan, to be Arnold to a troop of savages, but to be one of them, where they are all selfish, lazy, and brutal." It is this universality of paganism which gives its main interest to such a study as the present. Paganism is a constant and not a temporary or local phase of human life and thought, and it has very little to do with the question of what particular dogmas a man may believe or reject.

Thus, for example, although the Greek is popularly accepted as the type of paganism and the Christian of idealism, yet the lines of that distinction have often been reversed. Christianity has at times become hard and cold and lifeless, and has swept away primitive national idealisms without supplying any new ones. The Roman ploughman must have missed the fauns whom he had been accustomed to expect in the thicket at the end of his furrrow, when the new faith told him that these were nothing but rustling leaves. When the swish of unseen garments beside the old nymph-haunted fountain was silenced, his heart was left lonely and his imagination impoverished. Much charm and romance vanished from his early world with the passing of its pagan creatures, and indeed it is to this cause that we must trace the extraordinarily far-reaching and varied crop of miraculous legends of all sorts which sprang up in early Catholic times. These were the protest of unconscious idealism against the bare world from which its sweet presences had vanished.

> "In th' olde dayes of the King Arthour,
> Of which that Britons speken greet honour,
> Al was this land fulfild of fayerye.
> The elf-queen, with hir joly companye,
> Daunced ful ofte in many a grene mede;
> This was the olde opinion, as I rede.
> But now can no man see none elves mo.
> For now the grete charitee and prayeres
> Of limitours and othere holy freres,
> . . . .
> This maketh that there been no fayeryes.
> For ther as wont to walken was an elf,
> Ther walketh now the limitour himself."

Against this impoverishment the human revolt was inevitable, and it explains the spirit in such writers as Shelley and Goethe. Children of nature, who love the sun and the grass, and are at home upon the earth, their spirits cry for something to delight and satisfy them, nearer than speculations of theology or cold pictures of heaven. Wordsworth, in his famous lines, has expressed the protest in the familiar words:—

> "Great God, I'd rather be
> A Pagan, suckled in a creed outworn;
> So might I, standing on this pleasant lea,
> Have glimpses that would make me less forlorn;
> Have sight of Proteus rising from the sea,
> Or hear old Triton blow his wreathèd horn."

The early classic thought which found its most perfect expression in the mythology of Greece was not originally or essentially pagan. It was humanistic, and represented the response of man's spirit to that free and beautiful spirit which he found in nature around him. All such symbolism of Greek religion as that of the worship of Dionysus and Ceres, shows this. In these cults the commonest things of life, the wine and corn wherewith man sustained himself, assumed a higher and richer meaning. Food and drink were not mere sensual gratifications, but divine gifts, as they are in the twenty-third Psalm; and the whole material world was a symbol and sacrament of spiritual realities and blessings. Similarly the ritual of Eleusis interpreted man's common life into a wonderful world of mystic spirituality. Thus there was a great fund of spiritual insight of the finest and most beautiful sort in the very heart of that life which has thoughtlessly been adopted as the type of paganism.

Yet the history of Greece affords the explanation and even the justification of the popular idea. The pagan who is in us all, tends ever to draw us downwards from sacramental and symbolic ways of thinking to the easier life of the body and the earth. On the one hand, for blood that is young and hot, the life of sense is overwhelming. On the other hand, for the weary toiler whose mind is untrained, the impression of the world is that of heavy clay. Each in his own way finds idealism difficult to retain. The spirituality of nature floats like a dream before the mind of poets, and is seen now and then in wistful glimpses by every one; but it needs some clearer and less elusive form, as well as some definite association with conscience, if it is to be defended against the pull of the green earth. It has been well said that, for the Greek, God was the view; but when the traveller goes forward into the view, he meets with many things which it is dangerous to identify with God. For the young spirit of the early times the temptation to earthliness was overwhelming. The world was fair, its gates were open, and its barriers all down. Men took from literature and from religion just as much of spirituality as they understood and as little as they desired, and the effect was swift and inevitable in that degeneration which reached its final form in the degraded sensuality of the later Roman Empire.

The confusing element in all such inquiry lies in the fact that one can never get an unmixed paganism nor a perfect idealism. Just as the claims of body and spirit are in our daily life inextricably interwoven, so the Greek thought hung precariously between the two, and was always more or less at the mercy of the individual interpreter and of the relative strength of his tastes and passions. So we shall find it all through the course of these studies. It would be preposterous to deny some sort of idealism to almost any pagan who has ever lived. The contrast between pagan and idealist is largely a matter of proportion and preponderating tendency: yet the lines are clear enough to enable us to work with this distinction and to find it valuable and illuminating.

The fundamental fact to remember in studying any of the myths of Greece is, that we have here a composite and not a simple system of thought and imagination. There are always at least two layers: the primitive, and the Olympian which came later. The primitive conceptions were those afforded by the worship of ghosts, of dead persons, and of animals. Miss Jane Harrison has pointed out in great detail the primitive elements which lingered on through the Olympian worship. Perhaps the most striking instance which she quotes is the Anthesteria, or festival of flowers, at the close of which the spirits were dismissed with the formula, "Depart, ye ghosts, the revels now are ended." Mr. Andrew Lang has suggested that the animals associated with gods and goddesses (such as the mouse which is found in the hand, or the hair, or beside the feet of the statues of Apollo, the owl of Minerva, etc.) are relics of the earlier worship. This would satisfactorily explain much of the disreputable element which lingered on side by side with the noble thoughts of Greek religion. The Olympians, a splendid race of gods, representing the highest human ideals, arrived with the Greeks; but for the sake of safety, or of old association, the primitive worship was retained and blended with the new. In the extreme case of human sacrifice, it was retained in the form of surrogates—little wooden images, or even actual animals, being sacrificed in lieu of the older victims. But all along the line, while the new gods brought their spiritual conceptions, the older ones held men to a cruder and more fleshly way of thinking. There is a similar blend of new and old in all such movements as that of the Holy Grail and the Arthurian legends, where we can see the combination of Christian and pagan elements so clearly as to be able to calculate the moral and spiritual effect of each. Thus we have in the early Greek mythology much of real paganism involved in the retention of the old and earth-bound gods which attached themselves to the nobler Olympians as they came, and dragged them down to the ancient level.

This blending may be seen very clearly in the mythology of Homer and Hesiod. There it has been so thorough that the only trace of superposition which we can find is the succession of the dynasties of Chronos and Jupiter. The result is the most appalling conception of the morality of celestial society. No earthly state could hope to continue for a decade upon the principles which governed the life of heaven ; and man, if he were to escape the sudden retributions which must inevitably follow anything like an imitation of his gods, must live more decently than they.

Now Homer was, in a sense, the Bible of the Greeks, and as society improved in morals, and thought was directed more and more fearlessly towards religious questions, the puzzle as to the immoralities of the gods became acute. The religious and intellectual developments of the sixth century B.C. led to various ways of explaining the old stories. Sophocles is conciliatory, conceiving religion in a sunny good temper which will make the best of the situation whatever it is. Æschylus is sombre and deeply tragic, while yet he remains orthodox on the side of the gods. But Euripides is angry at the old scandals, and in the name of humanity his scepticism rises in protest.

It may be interesting, at this point, to glance for a little at the various theories which have been brought forward to explain the myths. The commonest of all such theories is that the divine personalities stand for the individual powers of nature. Most especially, the gods and goddesses symbolise the sun, moon, and stars, night and morning, summer and winter, and the general story of the year. No one will deny that the personification of Nature had a large share in all mythology. The Oriental mythologies rose to a large extent in this fashion. The Baals of Semitic worship all stood for one or other of the manifestations of the fructifying powers of nature, and the Chinese dragon is the symbol of the spiritual mystery of life suggested by the mysterious and protean characteristics of water. It is very natural that this should be so, and every one who has ever felt the power of the sun in the East will sympathise with Turner's dying words, " The sun, he is God."

As a key to mythology this theory was especially associated with the name of Plutarch among ancient writers, and it has been accepted more or less completely by a vast number of moderns. In the late Sir George Cox's fascinating stories it was run to utter absurdity. The story is beautifully told in every case, and when we have enjoyed it and felt something of the exquisiteness of the conception and of the variety and range of thought exhibited in the fertile minds of those who had first told it, Sir George Cox draws us back sharply to the assertion that all we have been hearing really meant another phase of sunset or sunrise, until we absolutely rebel and protest that the effect is unaccountable upon so meagre a cause. It is an easy method of dealing with folk-lore. If you take the rhyme of Mary and her little lamb, and call Mary the sun and the lamb the moon, you will achieve astonishing results, both in religion and astronomy, when you find that the lamb followed Mary to school one day. This nature element, however, had undoubtedly a very considerable part in the origin of myths, and when Max Müller combines it with philology it opens a vast field of extraordinarily interesting interpretations resting upon words and their changes.

A further theory of myths is that which regards them as the stories of races told as if they had been the lives of individuals. This, as is well known, has had permanent effects upon the interpretation not only of Greek but of Hebrew ancient writings, and it throws light upon some of those chapters of Genesis which, without it, are but strings of forgotten and unpronounceable names.

But beyond all such explanations, after we have allowed for them in every possible way, there remains a conviction that behind these fascinating stories there is a certain irreducible remainder of actual fact. Individual historic figures, seen through the mists of time, walk before our eyes in the dawn. Long before history was written men lived and did striking deeds. Heroic memories and traditions of such distinguished men passed in the form of fireside tales from one generation to another through many centuries. Now they come to us, doubtless hugely exaggerated and so far away from their originals as to be unrecognisable, and yet, after all, based upon things that happened. For the stories have living touches in them which put blood into the glorious and ghostly figures, and when we come upon a piece of genuine human nature there is no possibility of mistaking it. This thing has been born, not manufactured: nor has any portrait that is life-like been drawn without some model. Thus, through all the mist and haze of the past, we see men and women walking in the twilight—dim and uncertain forms indeed, yet stately and heroic.

Now all this has a bearing upon the main subject of our present study. Meteorology and astronomy are indeed noble sciences, but the proper study of mankind is man. While, no doubt, the sources of all early folk-lore are composite, yet it matters greatly for the student of these things whether the beginnings of religious thought were merely in the clouds, or whether they had their roots in the same earth whereon we live and labour. The heroes and great people of the early days are eternal figures, because each new generation gives them a resurrection in its own life and experience. They have eternal human meanings, beneath whatever pageantry of sun and stars the ancient heroes passed from birth to death. Soon everything of them is forgotten except the ideas about human life for which they stand. Then each of them becomes the expression of a thought common to humanity, and therefore secure of its immortality to the end of time; for the undying interest is the human interest, and all ideas which concern the life of man are immortal while man's race lasts. In the case of such legends as those we are discussing, it is probable that beyond the mere story some such ideal of human life was suggested from the very first. Certainly, as time went on, the ideal became so identified with the hero, that to thoughtful men he came to stand for a particular idealism of human experience. Thus Pater speaks of Dionysus as from first to last a type of second birth, opening up the hope of a possible analogy between the resurrections of nature and something else, reserved for human souls. "The beautiful, weeping creatures, vexed by the wind, suffering, torn to pieces, and rejuvenescent again at last, like a tender shoot of living green out of the hardness and stony darkness of the earth, becomes an emblem or ideal of chastening and purification, and of final victory through suffering." This theory would also explain the fact that one nation's myths are not only similar to, but to a large extent practically identical with, those of other nations. There is a common stock of ideas supplied by the common elements of human nature in all lands and times; and these, when finely expressed, produce a common fund of ideals which will appeal to the majority of the human race.

Thus mythology was originally simple story-telling. But men, even in the telling of the story, began to find meanings for it beyond the mere narration of events; and thus there arose in connection with all stories that were early told, a certain number of judgments of what was high and admirable in human nature. These were not grounded upon philosophical or scientific bases, but upon the bed-rock of man's experience. Out of these judgments there grew the great ideals which from first to last have commanded the spirit of man.

In this connection it is interesting to remember that in Homer the men were regarded as the means of revealing ideas and characters, and not as mere natural objects in themselves. The things among which they lived are described and known by their appearances; the men are known by their words and deeds. "There is no inventory of the features of men, or of fair women, as there is in the Greek poets of the decline or in modern novels. Man is something different from a curious bit of workmanship that delights the eye. He is a 'speaker of words and a doer of deeds,' and his true delineation is in speech and action, in thought and emotion." Thus, from the first, ideas are the central and important element. They spring from and cling to stories of individual human lives, and the finest of them become ideals handed down for the guidance of the future race. The myths, with their stories of gods and men, and their implied or declared religious doctrines, are but the forms in which these ideals find expression. The ideals remain, but the forms of their expression change, advancing from cruder to finer and from more fanciful to more exactly true, with the advance of thought and culture. Meanwhile, the ideals are above the world,—dwelling, like Plato's, in heaven, —and there are always two alternatives for every man. He may go back either with deliberate intellectual assent, or passion-led in sensual moods, to the powers of nature and the actual human stories in their crude and earthly form; or he may follow the idealisation of human experience, and discover and adopt the ideals of which the earthly stories and the nature processes are but shadows and hints. In the former case he will be a pagan; in the latter, a spiritual idealist. In what remains of this lecture, we shall consider four of the most famous Greek legends—those of Prometheus, Medusa, Orpheus, and Apollo—in the light of what has just been stated.

Prometheus, in the early story, is a Titan, who in the heavenly war had fought on the side of Zeus. It is, however, through the medium of the later story that Prometheus has exercised his eternal influence upon the thought of men. In this form of the legend he appears constantly living and striving for man's sake as the foe of God. We hear of him making men and women of clay and animating them with celestial fire, teaching them the arts of agriculture, the taming of horses, and the uses of plants. Again we hear of Zeus, wearied with the race of men—the new divinity making a clean sweep, and wishing to begin with better material. Zeus is the lover of strength and the despiser of weakness, and from the earth with its weak and pitiful mortals he takes away the gift of fire, leaving them to perish of cold and helplessness. Then it is that Prometheus climbs to heaven, steals back the fire in his hollow cane, and brings it down to earth again. For this benefaction to the despised race Zeus has him crucified, fixed for thirty thousand years on a rock in the Asian Caucasus, where, until Herakles comes to deliver him, the vulture preys upon his liver.

Such a story tempts the allegorist, and indeed the main drift of its meaning is unmistakable. Cornutus, a contemporary of Christ, explained it "of forethought, the quick inventiveness of human thought chained to the painful necessities of human life, its liver gnawed unceasingly by cares." In the main, and as a general description, this is quite unquestionable. Prometheus is the prototype of a thousand other figures of the same kind, not in mythology only, but in history, which tell the story of the spiritual effort of man frustrated and brought to earth. It is the story of Tennyson's youth who

> "Rode a horse with wings that would have flown
> But that his heavy rider bore him down."

Only, in the Prometheus idea, it is not a man's own senses, as in Tennyson's poem, but the outward necessity of things, the heavy and cruel powers of nature around him, that prove too much for his aspirations. In this respect the story is singularly characteristic of the Greek spirit. That spirit was always daring with truth, feeling the risks of knowledge and gladly taking them, passionately devoted to the love of knowledge for its own sake.

The legend has, however, a deeper significance than this. One of the most elemental questions that man can ask is, What is the relation of the gods to human inquiry and freedom of thought? There always has been a school of thinkers who have regarded knowledge as a thing essentially against the gods. The search for knowledge thus becomes a phase of Titanism; and wherever it is found, it must always be regarded in the light of a secret treasure stolen from heaven against the will of contemptuous or jealous divinities. On the other hand, knowledge is obviously the friend of man. Prometheus is man's champion, and no figure could make a stronger appeal than his. Indeed, in not a few respects he approaches the Christian ideal, and must have brought in some measure the same solution to those who were able to receive it. Few touches in literature, for instance, are finer than that in which he comforts the daughters of Ocean, speaking to them from his cross.

The idea of Titanism has become the commonplace of poets. It is familiar in Milton, Byron, Shelley, and countless others, and Goethe tells us that the fable of Prometheus lived within him. Many of the Titanic figures, while they appeared to be blaspheming, were really fighting for truth and justice. The conception of the gods as jealous and contemptuous was not confined to the Greek mythology, but has appeared within the pale of Christian faith as well as in all heathen cults. Nature, in some of its aspects, seems to justify it. The great powers appear to be arrayed against man's efforts, and present the appearance of cruel and bullying strength. Evidently upon such a theory something must go, either our faith in God or our faith in humanity; and when faith has gone we shall be left in the position either of atheists or of slaves. There have been those who accepted the alternative and went into the one camp or the other according to their natures; but the Greek legend did not necessitate this. There was found, as in Æschylus, a hint of reconciliation, which may be taken to represent that conviction so deep in the heart of humanity, that there is "ultimate decency in things," if one could only find it out; although knowledge must always remain dangerous, and may at times cost a man dear.

The real secret lies in the progress of thought in its conceptions of God and life. Nature, as we know and experience it, presents indeed an appalling spectacle against which everything that is good in us protests. God, so long as He is but half understood, is utterly unpardonable; and no man yet has succeeded in justifying the ways of God to men. But "to understand all is to forgive all"—or rather, it is to enter into a larger view of life, and to discover how much there is in *us* that needs to be forgiven. This is the wonderful story which was told by the Hebrews so dramatically in their Book of Job; and the phases through which that drama passes might be taken as the completest commentary on the myth of Prometheus which ever has been or can be written.

In two great battlegrounds of the human spirit the problem raised by Prometheus has been fought out. On the ground of science, who does not know the defiant and Titanic mood in which knowledge has at times been sought? The passion for knowing flames through the gloom and depression and savagery of the darker moods of the student. Difficulties are continually thrust into the way of knowledge. The upper powers seem to be jealous and outrageously thwarting, and the path of learning becomes a path of tears and blood. That is all that has been reached by many a grim and brave student spirit. But there is another possible explanation; and there are those who have attained to a persuasion that the gods have made knowledge difficult in order that the wise may also be the strong.

The second battleground is that of philanthropy. Here also there has been an apparently reasonable Titanism. Men have struggled in vain, and then protested in bitterness, against the waste and the meaninglessness of the human *débâcle*. The only aspect of the powers above them has seemed to many noble spirits that of the sheer cynic. He that sitteth in the heavens must be laughing indeed. In Prometheus the Greek spirit puts up its daring plea for man. It pleads not for pity merely, but for the worth of human nature. The strong gods cannot be justified in oppressing man upon the plea that might is right, and that they may do what they please. The protest of Prometheus, echoed by Browning's protest of Ixion, appeals to the conscience of the world as right; and, kindling a noble Titanism, puts the divine oppressor in the wrong. Finally, there dawns over the edge of the ominous dark, the same hope that Prometheus vaguely hinted to the Greek. To him who has understood the story of Calvary, the ultimate interpretation of all human suffering is divine love. That which the cross of Prometheus in all its outrageous cruelty yet hints as in a whisper, the Cross of Christ proclaims to the end of time, shouting down the centuries from its blood and pain that God is love, and that in all our affliction He is afflicted.

Another myth of great beauty and far-reaching significance is that of Medusa. It is peculiarly interesting on account of its double edge, for it shows us both the high possibilities of ideal beauty and the deepest depths of pagan horror. Robert Louis Stevenson tells us how, as he hung between life and death in a flooded river of France, looking around him in the sunshine and seeing all the lovely landscape, he suddenly felt the attack of the other side of things. "The devouring element in the universe had leaped out against me, in this green valley quickened by a running stream. The bells were all very pretty in their way, but I had heard some of the hollow notes of *Pan's* music. Would the wicked river drag me down by the heels, indeed? and look so beautiful all the time?" It was in this connection that he gave us that striking and most suggestive phrase, "The beauty and the terror of the world." It is this combination of beauty and terror for which the myth of

Medusa stands. It finds its meaning in a thousand instances. On the one hand, it is seen in such ghastly incidents as those in which the sheer horror of nature's action, or of man's crime, becomes invested with an illicit beauty, and fascinates while it kills. On the other hand, it is seen in all of the many cases in which exquisite beauty proves also to be dangerous, or at least sinister. "The haunting strangeness in beauty" is at once one of the most characteristic and one of the most tragic things in the world.

There were three sisters, the Gorgons, who dwelt in the Far West, beyond the stream of ocean, in that cold region of Atlas where the sun never shines and the light is always dim. Medusa was one of them, the only mortal of the trio. She was a monster with a past, for in her girlhood she had been the beautiful priestess of Athene, golden-haired and very lovely, whose life had been devoted to virgin service of the goddess. Her golden locks, which set her above all other women in the desire of Neptune, had been her undoing: and when Athene knew of the frailty of her priestess, her vengeance was indeed appalling. Each lock of the golden hair was transformed into a venomous snake. The eyes that had been so love-inspiring were now bloodshot and ferocious. The skin, with its rose and milk-white tenderness, had changed to a loathsome greenish white. All that remained of Medusa was a horrid thing, a mere grinning mask with protruding beast-like tusks and tongue hanging out. So dreadful was the aspect of the changed priestess, that her face turned all those who chanced to catch sight of it to stone. There is a degree of hideousness which no eyes can endure; and so it came to pass that the cave wherein she dwelt, and all the woods around it, were full of men and wild beasts who had been petrified by a glance of her,—grim fossils immortalised in stone,—while the snakes writhed and the red eyes rolled, waiting for another victim.

This was not a case into which any hope of redemption could enter, and there was nothing for it but to slay her. To do this, Perseus set out upon his long journey, equipped with the magic gifts of swiftness and invisibility, and bearing on his arm the shield that was also a mirror. The whole picture is infinitely dreary. As he travels across the dark sea to the land where the pillars of Atlas are visible far off, towering into the sky, the light decreases. In the murky and dangerous twilight he forces the Graiai, those grey-haired sisters with their miserable fragmentary life, to bestir their aged limbs and guide him to the Gorgons' den. By the dark stream, where the yellow light brooded everlastingly, he reached at last that cave of horrors. Well was it then for Perseus that he was invisible, for the snakes that were Medusa's hair could see all round. But at that time Medusa was asleep and the snakes asleep, and in the silence and twilight of the land where there is "neither night nor day, nor cloud nor breeze nor storm," he held the magic mirror over against the monster, beheld her in it without change or injury to himself, severed the head, and bore it away to place it on Athene's shield.

It is very interesting to notice how Art has treated the legend. It was natural that so vivid an image should become a favourite alike with poets and with sculptors, but there was a gradual development from the old hideous and terrible representations, back to the calm repose of a beautiful dead face. This might indeed more worthily record the maiden's tragedy, but it missed entirely the thing that the old myth had said. The oldest idea was horrible beyond horror, for the darker side of things is always the most impressive to primitive man, and sheer ugliness is a category with which it is easy to work on simple minds. The rudest art can achieve such grotesque hideousness long before it can depict beauty. Later, as we have seen, Art tempered the face to beauty, but in so doing forgot the meaning of the story. It was the old story that has been so often told, of the fair and frail one who had fallen among the pitiless. For her there was no compassion either in mortals or in immortals. It was the tragedy of sweet beauty desecrated and lost, the petrifying horror of which has found its most unflinching modern expression in Thomas Hardy's *Tess of the D'Urbervilles. Corruptio optimi pessima.*

To interpret such stories as these by any reference to the rising sun, or the rivalry between night and dawn, is simply to stultify the science of interpretation. It may, indeed, have been true that most of those who told and heard the tale in ancient times accepted it in its own right, and without either the desire or the thought of further meanings. Yet, even told in that fashion, as it clung to memory and imagination, it must continually have reminded men of certain features of essential human nature, which it but too evidently recorded. Here was one of the sad troop of soulless women who appear in the legends of all the races of mankind. Medusa had herself been petrified before she turned others to stone. The horror that had come upon her life had been too much to bear, and it had killed her heart within her.

So far of passion and the price the woman's heart has paid for it. But this story has to do also with Athene, on whose shield Medusa's head must rest at last. For it is not passion only, but knowledge, that may petrify the soul. Indeed, the story of passion can only do this when the dazzling glamour of temptation has passed, and in place of it has come the cold knowledge of remorse. Then the sight of one's own shame, and, on a wider scale, the sight of the pain and the tragedy of the world, present to the eyes of every generation the spectacle of victims standing petrified like those who had seen too much at the cave's mouth in the old legend.

It is peculiarly interesting to contrast the story of Medusa with its Hebrew parallel in Lot's wife. Both are women presumably beautiful, and both are turned to stone. But while the Greek petrifaction is the result of too direct a gaze upon the horrible, the Hebrew is the result of too loving and desirous a gaze upon the coveted beauty of the world. Nothing could more exactly represent and epitomise the diverse genius of the nations, and we understand the Greek story the better for the strong contrast with its Hebrew parallel. To the Greek, ugliness was dangerous; and the horror of the world, having no explanation nor redress, could but petrify the heart of man. To the Hebrew, the beauty of the world was dangerous, and man must learn to turn away his eyes from beholding vanity.

The legend of Medusa is a story of despair, and there is little room in it for idealism of any kind; and yet there may be some hint, in the reflecting shield of Perseus, of a brighter and more heartening truth. The horror of the world we have always with us, and for all exquisite spirits like those of the Greeks there is the danger of their being marred by the brutality of the universe, and made hard and cold in rigid petrifaction by the too direct vision of evil. Yet for such spirits there is ever some shield of faith, in whose reflection they may see the darkest horrors and yet remain flesh and blood. Those who believe in life and love, whose religion—or at least whose indomitable clinging to the beauty they have once descried—has taught them sufficient courage in dwelling upon these things, may come unscathed through any such ordeal. But for that, the story is one of sheer pagan terror. It came out of the old, dark pre-Olympian mythology (for the Gorgons are the daughters of Hades), and it embodied the ancient truth that the sorrow of the world worketh death. It is a tragic world, and the earth-bound, looking upon its tragedy, will see in it only the *macabre*, and feel that graveyard and spectral air which breathes about the haunted pagan sepulchre.

Another myth in which we see the contrast between essential paganism and idealism is that of Orpheus. The myth appears in countless forms and with innumerable excrescences, but in the main it is in three successive parts. The first of these tells of the sweet singer loved by all the creatures, the dear friend of all the world, whose charm nothing that lived on earth could resist, and whose spell hurt no creature whom it allured. The conception stands in sharp contrast to the ghastly statuary that adorned Medusa's precincts. Here, with a song whose sweetness surpassed that of the Sirens, nature, dead and living both (for all lived unto Orpheus), followed him with glad and loving movement. Nay, not only beasts and trees, but stones themselves and even mountains, felt in the hard heart of them the power of this sweet music. It is one of the most perfect stories ever told—the precursor of the legends that gathered round Francis of Assisi and many a later saint and artist. It is the prophecy from the earliest days of that consummation of which Isaiah was afterwards to sing and St. Paul to echo the song, when nature herself would come to the perfect reconciliation for which she had been groaning and travailing through all the years.

The second part of the story tells of the tragedy of love. Such a man as Orpheus, if he be fortunate in his love, will love wonderfully, and Eurydice is his worthy bride. Dying, bitten by a snake in the grass as she flees from danger, she descends to Hades. But the surpassing love of the sweet singer dares to enter that august shadow, not to drink the Waters of Lethe only and to forget, but also to drink the waters of Eunoe and to remember. His music charms the dead, and those who have the power of death. Even the hard-hearted monarch of hell is moved for Orpheus, who

"Drew iron tears down Pluto's cheek,
And made hell grant what love did seek."

But the rescue has one condition. He must restrain himself, must not look upon the face of his beloved though he bears her in his arms, until they have passed the region of the shadow of death, and may see one another in the sunlight of the bright earth again. The many versions of the tragic disobedience to this condition bear eloquent testimony, not certainly to any changing phase of the sky, but to the manifold aspects of human life. According to some accounts, it was the rashness of Orpheus that did the evil—love's impatience, that could not wait the fitting time, and, snatching prematurely that which was its due, sacrificed all. According to other accounts, it was Eurydice who tempted Orpheus, her love and pain having grown too hungry and blind. However that may be, the error was fatal, and on the very eve of victory all was lost. It was lost, not by any snatching back in which strong hands of hell tore his beloved from the man's grasp. Within his arms the form of Eurydice faded away, and as he clutched at her his fingers closed upon the empty air. That, too, is a law deep in the nature of things. It is by no arbitrary decree that self-restraint has been imposed on love. In this, as in all other things, a man must consent to lose his life in order to find it; and those who will not accept the conditions, will be visited by no melodramatic or violent catastrophe. Love which has broken law will simply fade away and vanish.

The third part of the story is no less interesting and significant. Maddened with this second loss, so irrevocable and yet due to so avoidable a cause, Orpheus, in restless despair, wandered about the lands. For him the nymphs had now no attractions, nor was there anything in all the world but the thought of his half-regained Eurydice, now lost for ever. His music indeed remained, nor did he cast away his lute; but it was heard only in the most savage and lonely places. At length wild Thracian women heard it, furious in the rites of Dionysus. They desired him, but his heart was elsewhere, and, in the mad reaction of their savage breasts, when he refused them they tore him limb from limb. He was buried near the river Hebrus, and his head was thrown into the stream. But as the waters bore it down, the lips whose singing had charmed the world still repeated the beloved name Eurydice to the waters as they flowed.

Here again it is as if, searching for the dead in some ancient sepulchre, we had found a living man and friend. The symbolism of the story, disentangled from detail which may have been true enough in a lesser way, is clear to every reader. It tells that love is strong as death—that old sweet assurance which the lover in Canticles also discovered. Love is indeed set here under conditions, or rather it has perceived the conditions which the order of things has set, and these conditions have been violated. But still the voice of the severed head, crying out the beloved name as the waters bore it to the sea, speaks in its own exquisite way the final word. It gives the same assurance with the same thrill which we feel when we read the story of Herakles wrestling with death for the body of Alkestis, and winning the woman back from her very tomb.

But before love can be a match for death, it first must conquer life, and the early story of the power of Orpheus over the wild beasts, restoring, as it does, an earthly paradise in which there is nothing but gentleness, marks the conquest of life by love. All life's wildness and savagery, which seem to give the lie to love continually, are after all conquerable, and may be tamed. And the lesson of it all is the great persuasion that in the depth of things life is good and not evil. When we come to the second conflict, and that love which has mastered life now pits itself against death, it goes forward to the greater adventure with a strange confidence. Who that has looked upon the face of one dearly beloved who is dead, has not known the leap of the spirit, not so much in rebellion as in demand? Love is so great a thing that it obviously ought to have this power, and somehow we are all persuaded that it has it—that death is but a puppet king, and love the master of the universe after all. The story of Orpheus and Eurydice is but a faltering expression of this great assurance, yet it does express it.

For it explains to all who have ears to hear, what are the real enemies of love which can weaken it in its conflict with death. The Thracian women, those drunken bacchanals that own no law but their desires, stand for the lawless claim and attack of the lower life upon the higher. They but repeat, in exaggerated and delirious form, the sad story of the forfeiture of Eurydice. It is the touch of lawlessness, of haste, of selfishness, that costs love its victory and finally slays it, so far as love can be slain.

In this wonderful story we have a pure Greek

creation in the form of one of the finest sagas of the world. The battle between the pagan and ideal aspects of life is seen in countless individual touches throughout the story; but the whole tale is one continuous symbolic warning against paganism, and a plea for idealism urged in the form of a mighty contrast. Love is here seen in its most spiritual aspect. Paganism enters with the touch of lawlessness. On the large scale the battle was fought out some centuries later, in the days of the Roman Empire, for all the world to see. The two things which give their character to the centuries from Augustus to Constantine are the persistent cry of man for immortality, and the strong lusts of the flesh which silenced it. On the smaller scale of each individual life, men and women will understand to the end of time, from their own experience, the story of Orpheus.

It is peculiarly interesting to remember that the figure of the sweet singer grew into the centre of a great religious creed. The cult of Orphism, higher and more spiritual than that of either Eleusis or Dionysus, appears as early as the sixth century B.C., and reaches its greatest in the fifth and fourth centuries. The Orphic hymns proclaim the high doctrine of the divineness of all life, and open, at least for the hopes of men, the gates of immortality.

The secret societies which professed the cult had the strongest possible influence upon the thought of early Athens, but their most prominent effect is seen in Plato, who derived from them his main doctrines of pre-existence, penance, reincarnation, and the final purification of the soul. Even the early Christians, who hated so bitterly many of the myths of paganism, and found in them nothing but doctrines of devils, treated this story tenderly, blended the picture of Orpheus with that of their own Good Shepherd, and found it edifying to Christian faith.

One more instance may be given in the story of Apollo, in which, more perhaps than in any other, there is an amazing combination of bad and good elements. On the one hand there are the innumerable immoralities and savageries that are found in all the records of mythology. On the other hand, he who flays Marsias alive and visits the earth with plagues is also the healer of men. He is the cosmopolitan god of the brotherhood of mankind, the spirit of wisdom whose oracle acknowledged and inspired Socrates, and, generally, the incarnation of the "glory of the Lord."

We cannot here touch upon the marvellous tales of Delos and of Delphi, nor repeat the strains that Pindar sang, sitting in his iron chair beside the shrine. This much at least we may say, that both the Apollo of Delos and the Apollo of Delphi are foreign gods, each of whom appropriated to his own use a sacred place where the ancient earth-bound religion had already established its rites. The Greeks brought with them a splendid god from their former home, but in his new shrine he was identified with a local god, very far from splendid; and this seems to be the most reasonable explanation of the inconsistency between the revolting and the beautiful elements in his worship. Pindar at least repudiated the relics of the poorer cult, and cried concerning such stories as were current then, "Oh, my tongue, fling this tale from thee; it is a hateful cleverness that slanders gods." No one who has realised the power and glory of the Eastern sun, can wonder at the identification both of the good and bad symbolism with the orb of day. Sun-worship is indeed a form of nature-worship, and there are physical reasons obvious enough for its being able to incorporate both the clean and unclean, both the deadly and the benign legends. Yet there is a splendour in it which is seen in its attraction for such minds as those of Aurelian and Julian, and which is capable of refinement in the delicate spirituality of Mithra, that worship of the essential principle of light, the soul of sunshine. In the worship of Apollo we have a combination, than which none on record is more striking, of the finest spirituality with the crudest paganism.

Here then, in the magical arena of the early world of Greece, we see in one of its most romantic forms the age-long strife between paganism and spirituality. We have taken at random four of the most popular stories of Greece. We have found in each of them pagan elements partly bequeathed by that earlier and lower earth-bound worship which preceded the Olympians, partly added in decadent days when the mind of man was turned from the heights and grovelling again. But we have seen a deeper meaning in them, far further-reaching than any story of days and nights or of years and seasons. It is a story of the aspiring spirit which is ever wistful here on the green earth (although that indeed is pleasant), and which finds its home among high thoughts, and ideas which dwell in heaven. We shall see many aspects of the same twofold thought and life, as we move about from point to point among the literature of later days. Yet we shall seldom find any phase of the conflict which has not been prophesied, or at least foreshadowed, in these legends of the dawn. The link that binds the earliest to the latest page of literature is just that human nature which, through all changes of country and of time, remains essentially the same. It is this which lends to our subject its individual as well as its historical interest. The battle is for each of us our own battle, and its victories and defeats are our own.

LECTURE II

MARIUS THE EPICUREAN

MUCH has been written, before and after the day of Walter Pater, concerning that singularly pure and yet singularly disappointing character, Marcus Aurelius, and his times. The ethical and religious ferment of the period has been described with great fullness and sympathy by Professor Dill. Yet it may be said, without fear of contradiction, that no book has ever been written, nor is likely ever to appear, which has conveyed to those who came under its spell a more intimate and familiar conception of that remarkable period and man than that which has been given by Walter Pater's *Marius the Epicurean*.

Opinion is divided about the value of Pater's work, and if it be true that some of his admirers have provoked criticism by their unqualified praise, it is no less true that many of his detractors appear never to have come in contact with his mind at all. Born in 1839, he spent the greater part of his life in Queen's College, Oxford, where he died in 1894. As literary critic, humanist, and master of a thoroughly original style, he made a considerable impression upon his generation from the first; but it may be safely said that it is only now, when readers are able to look upon his work in a more spacious and leisurely way, that he and his contribution to English thought and letters have come to their own.

The family was of Dutch extraction, and while the sons of his grandfather were trained in the Roman Catholic religion, the daughters were Protestants from their childhood. His father left the Roman Catholic communion early in life, without adopting any other form of Christian faith. It is not surprising that out of so strongly marked and widely mingled a heredity there should have emerged a writer prone to symbolism and open to the sense of beauty in ritual, and yet too cosmopolitan to accept easily the conventional religious forms. Before his twentieth year he had come under the influence of Ruskin's writings, but he soon parted from that wayward and contradictory master, whose brilliant dogmatism enslaved so thoroughly, but so briefly, the taste of young England. Ruskin, however, had awakened Pater, although to a style of criticism very different from his own, and for this service we owe him much.

The environment of Oxford subjected his spirit to two widely different sets of influences. On the one hand, he was in contact with such men as Jowett, Nettleship, and Thomas Hill Green: on the other hand, with Swinburne, Burne-Jones, and the pre-Raphaelites. Thus the awakened spirit felt the dominion both of a high spiritual rationalism, and of the beauty of flesh and the charm of the earth. A visit to Italy in company with Shadwell, and his study of the Renaissance there, made him an enthusiastic humanist. The immediate product of this second awakening was the *Renaissance* Essays, a very remarkable volume of his early work. Twelve years later, *Marius the Epicurean*, his second book, appeared in 1885. In Dr. Gosse, Pater has found an interpreter of rare sympathy and insight, whose appreciations of his contemporaries are, in their own right, fine contributions to modern literature.

The characteristics of his style were also those both of his thought and of his character. Dr. Gosse has summed up the reserve and shy reticence and the fastidious taste which always characterise his work, in saying that he was "one of the most exquisite, most self-respecting, the most individual prose writers of the age." Even in the matter of style he consciously respected his own individuality, refusing to read either Stevenson or Kipling for fear that their masterful strength might lead him out of his path. Certainly his bitterest enemies could not accuse him of borrowing from either of them. Mr. Kipling is apt to sacrifice everything to force, while Pater is perhaps the gentlest writer of our time. In Stevenson there is a delicate and yet vigorous human passion, but also a sense of fitness, a consciousness of style that is all his own. He is preaching, and not swearing at you, as you often feel Mr. Kipling to be doing. To preach at one may be indeed to take a great liberty, but of course much will depend upon whether the preaching is good preaching. Be that as it may, Pater is distinctive, and borrows nothing from any writer whose influence can be traced in his work. He neither swears nor preaches, but weaves about his reader a subtle film of thought, through whose gossamer all things seem to suffer a curious change, and to become harmonious and suggestive, as dark and quiet-coloured things often are. The writer does not force himself upon his readers, nor tempt even the most susceptible to imitate him; rather he presupposes himself, and dominates without appearing. His reticence, to which we have already referred, is one of his most characteristic qualities. Dr. Gosse ascribes it to a somewhat low and sluggish vitality of physical spirits. For one in this condition "the first idea in the presence of anything too vivacious is to retreat, and the most obvious form of social retreat is what we call affectation." That Pater's style has impressed many readers as affected there can be no question, and it is as unquestionable that Dr. Gosse's explanation is the true one.

His style has been much abused by critics who have found it easy to say smart things about such tempting peculiarities. We may admit at once that the writing is laboured and shows constant marks of the tool. The same criticism applies, for that matter, to much that Stevenson has written. But unless a man's style is absolutely offensive, which Pater's emphatically is not, it is a wise rule to accept it rather as a revelation of the man than as a chance for saying clever things. As one reads the work of some of our modern critics, one cannot but perceive and regret how much of pleasure and of profit their cleverness has cost them. Acknowledging his laboriousness and even his affectation, we still maintain that the style of Walter Pater is a very adequate expression of his mind. There is a calm suggestive atmosphere, a spirit half-childish and half-aged about his work. It is the work of a solemn and sensitive child, who has kept the innocence of his eye for impressions, and yet brought to his speech the experience, not of years only, but of centuries. He has many things to teach directly; but even when he is not teaching so, the air you breathe with its delicate suggestion of faint odours, the perfect taste in selection, the preferences and shrinkings and shy delights, all proclaim a real and high culture. And, after all, the most notable point in his style is just its exactness. Over-precise it may be sometimes, and even meticulous, yet that is because it is the exact expression of a delicate and subtle mind. In his *Appreciations* he lays down, as a first canon for style, Flaubert's principle of the search, the unwearied search, not for the smooth, or winsome, or forcible word as such, but, quite simply and honestly, for the word's adjustment to its meaning. It will be said in reply to any such defence that the highest art is to conceal art. That is an old saying and a hard one, and it is not possible to apply its rule in every instance. Pater's immense sense of the value of words, and his choice of exact expressions, resulted in language marvellously adapted to indicate the almost inexpressible shades of thought. When a German struggles for the utterance of some mental complexity he fashions new compounds of words; a Frenchman helps out his meaning by gesture, as the Greek long ago did by tone. Pater knows only one way of overcoming such situations, and that is by the painful search for the unique word that he ought to use.

One result of this habit is that he has enriched our literature with a large number of pregnant phrases which, it is safe to prophesy, will take their place in the vernacular of literary speech. "Hard gem-like flame," "Drift of flowers," "Tacitness of mind,"—such are some memorable examples of the exact expression of elusive ideas. The house of literature built in this fashion is a notable achievement in the architecture of language. It reminds us of his own description of a temple of Æsculapius: "His heart bounded as the refined and dainty magnificence of the place came upon him suddenly, in the flood of early sunshine, with the ceremonial lights burning here and there, and with all the singular expression of sacred order, a surprising cleanliness and simplicity." Who would not give much to be able to say the thing he wants to say so exactly and so beautifully as that is said? Indeed the love of beauty is the key both to the humanistic thought and to the simple and lingering style of Pater's writing. If it is not always obviously simple, that is never due either to any vagueness or confusion of thought, but rather to a struggle to express precise shades of meaning which may be manifold, but which are perfectly clear to himself.

A mind so sensitive to beauty and so fastidious in judging of it and expressing it, must necessarily afford a fine arena for the conflict between the tendencies of idealism and paganism. Here the great struggle between conscience and desire, the rivalry of culture and restraint, the choice between Athens and Jerusalem, will present a peculiarly interesting spectacle. In Walter Pater both elements are strongly marked. The love of ritual, and a constitutional delight in solemnities of all kinds, was engrained in his nature. The rationalism of Green and Jowett, with its high spirituality lighting it from within, drove off the ritual for a time at least. The result of these various elements is a humanism for which he abandoned the profession of Christianity with which he had begun. Yet he could not really part from that earlier faith, and for a time he was, as Dr. Gosse has expressed it, "not all for Apollo, and not all for Christ." The same writer quotes as applicable to him an interesting phrase of Daudet's, "His brain was a disaffected cathedral," and likens him to that mysterious face of Mona Lisa, of whose fantastic enigma Pater himself has given the most brilliant and the most intricate description. From an early Christian idealism, through a period of humanistic paganism, he passed gradually and naturally back to the abandoned faith again, but in readopting it he never surrendered the humanistic gains of the time between. He accepted in their fullness both ideals, and so spiritualised his humanism and humanised his idealism. Anything less rich and complete than this could never have satisfied him. Self-denial is obviously not an end in itself; and yet the real end, the fulfilment of nature, can never by any possibility be attained by directly aiming at it, but must ever involve self-denial as a means towards its attainment. It is Pater's clear sight of the necessity of these two facts, and his lifelong attempt to reconcile them, that give him, from the ethical and religious point of view, his greatest importance.

The story of this reconciliation is *Marius the Epicurean*. It is a spiritual biography telling the inner history of a Roman youth of the time of Marcus Aurelius. It begins with an appreciative interpretation of the old Roman religion as it was then, and depicts the family celebrations by which the devout were wont to seek "to produce an agreement with the gods." Among the various and beautiful tableaux of that Roman life, we see the solemn thoughtful boy reading hard and becoming a precocious idealist, too old already for his years, but relieving the inward tension by much pleasure in the country and the open air. A time of delicate health brings him and us to a temple of Æsculapius. The priesthood there is a kind of hospital college brotherhood, whose teaching and way of life inculcate a mysteriously sacramental character in all matters of health and the body.

Like all other vital youths, Marius must eat of the tree of knowledge and become a questioner of hitherto accepted views. "The tyrannous reality of things visible," and all the eager desire and delight of youth, make their strong appeal. Two influences favour the temptation. First there is his friend, Flavian the Epicurean, of the school that delights in pleasure without afterthought, and is free from the burden and restraint of conscience; and later on, *The Golden Book* of Apuleius, with its exquisite story of Cupid and Psyche, and its search for perfectness in the frankly material life. The moral of its main story is that the soul must not look upon the face of its love, nor seek to analyse too closely the elements from which it springs. Spirituality will be left desolate if it breaks this ban, and its wiser course is to enjoy without speculation. Thus we see the youth drawn earthwards, yet with a clinging sense of far mystic reaches, which he refuses as yet to explore. The death of Flavian rudely shatters this phase of his experience, and we find him face to face with death. The section begins with the wonderful hymn of the Emperor Hadrian to his dying soul—

> Dear wanderer, gipsy soul of mine,
> Sweet stranger, pleasing guest and comrade of my flesh,
> Whither away? Into what new land,
> Pallid one, stoney one, naked one?

But the sheer spectacle and fact of death is too violent an experience for such sweet consolations, and the death of Flavian comes like a final revelation of nothing less than the soul's extinction. Not unnaturally, the next phase is a rebound into epicureanism, spiritual indeed in the sense that it could not stoop to low pleasures, but living wholly in the present none the less, with a strong and imperative appreciation of the fullness of earthly life.

The next phase of the life of Marius opens with a journey to Rome, during which he meets a second friend, the soldier Cornelius. This very distinctly drawn character fascinates the eye from the first. In him we meet a kind of earnestness which seems to interpret and fit in with the austere aspects of the landscape. It is different from that disciplined hardness which was to be seen in Roman soldiers as the result of their military training; indeed, it seems as if this were some new kind of knighthood, whose mingled austerity and blitheness were strangely suggestive of hitherto unheard-of achievements in character.

The impression made by Rome upon the mind of Marius was a somewhat morbid one. He was haunted more or less by the thought of its passing and its eventual ruin, and he found much, both in its religion and its pleasure, to criticise. The dominant figure in the imperial city was that of Marcus Aurelius the Emperor, so famous in his day that for two hundred years after his death his image was cherished among the Penates of many pious families. Amid much that was admirable in him, there was a certain chill in his stoicism, and a sense of lights fading out into the night. His words in praise of death, and much else of his, had of course a great distinction. Yet in his private intercourse with Marcus Aurelius, Marius was not satisfied, nor was it the bleak sense that all is vanity which troubled him, but rather a feeling of mediocrity—of a too easy acceptance of the world—in the imperial philosophy. For in the companionship of Cornelius there was a foil to the stoicism of Marcus Aurelius, and his friend was more truly an aristocrat than his Emperor. Cornelius did not accept the world in its entirety, either sadly or otherwise. In him there was "some inward standard . . . of distinction, selection, refusal, amid the various elements of the period and the corrupt life across which they were moving together." And, apparently as a consequence of this spirit of selection, "with all the severity of Cornelius, there was a breeze of hopefulness—freshness and hopefulness—as of new morning, about him." Already, it may be, the quick intelligence of the reader has guessed what is coming. Jesus Christ said of Himself on one occasion, "For distinctions I am come into the world." Marius' criticism of the Emperor reached its climax in his disgust at the amusements of the amphitheatre, which also Marcus Aurelius accepted.

There follows a long account of Roman life and thought, with much speculation as to the ideal commonwealth. That dream of the philosophers remains for ever in the air, detached from actual experiences and institutions, but Marius felt himself passing beyond it to something in which it would be actually realised and visibly localised, "the unseen Rome on high." Thus in correcting and supplementing the philosophies, and in insisting upon some actual embodiment of them on the earth, he is groping his way point by point to Christ. The late Dean Church has said: "No one can read the wonderful sayings of Seneca, Epictetus, or Marcus Aurelius, without being impressed, abashed perhaps, by their grandeur. No one can read them without wondering the next moment why they fell so dead—how little response they seem to have awakened round them." It is precisely at this point that the young Christian Church found its opportunity. Pagan idealisms were indeed in the air. The Christian idealism was being realised upon the earth, and it was this with which Marius was now coming into contact.

So he goes on until he is led up to two curious houses. The first of these was the house of Apuleius, where in a subtle and brilliant system of ideas it seemed as if a ladder had been set up from earth to heaven. But Marius discovered that what he wanted was the thing itself and not its mere theory, a life of realised ideals and not a dialectic. The second house was more curious still. Much pains is spent upon the description of it with its "quiet signs of wealth, and of a noble taste," in which both colour and form, alike of stones and flowers, seemed expressive of a rare and potent beauty in the personality that inhabited them. There were inscriptions there to the dead martyrs, inscriptions full of confidence and peace. Old pagan symbols were there also—Herakles wrestling with death for possession of Alkestis, and Orpheus taming the wild beasts—blended naturally with new symbols such as the Shepherd and the sheep, and the Good Shepherd carrying the sick lamb upon his shoulder. The voice of singers was heard in the house of an evening singing the candle hymn, "Hail, Heavenly Light." Altogether there seemed here to be a combination of exquisite and obvious beauty with "a transporting discovery of some fact, or series of facts, in which the old puzzle of life had found its solution."

It was none other than the Church of the early Christian days that Marius had stumbled on, under the guidance of his new friend; and already in heart he had actually become a Christian without knowing it, for these friends of comeliness seemed to him to have discovered the secret of actualising the ideal as none others had done. At such a moment in his spirituul career it is not surprising that he should hesitate to look upon that which would "define the critical turning-point," yet he looked. He saw the blend of Greek and Christian, each at its best—the martyrs' hope, the singers' joy and health. In this "minor peace of the Church," so pure, so delicate, and so vital that it made the Roman life just then "seem like some stifling forest of bronze-work, transformed, as if by malign enchantment, out of the generations of living trees," he seemed to see the possibility of satisfaction at last. For here there was a perfect love and self-sacrifice, outwardly expressed with a mystic grace better than the Greek blitheness, and a new beauty which contrasted brightly with the Roman insipidity. It was the humanism of Christianity that so satisfied him, standing as it did for the fullness of life, in spite of all its readiness for sacrifice. And it was effective too, for it seemed to be doing rapidly what the best paganism was doing very slowly—attaining, almost without thinking about it, the realisation of the noblest ideals.

"And so it came to pass that on this morning Marius saw for the first time the wonderful spectacle—wonderful, especially, in its evidential power over himself, over his own thoughts—of those who believe. There were noticeable, among those present, great varieties of rank, of age, of personal type. The Roman *ingenuus*, with the white toga and gold ring, stood side by side with his slave; and the air of the whole company was, above all, a grave one, an air of recollection. Coming thus unexpectedly upon this large assembly, so entirely united, in a silence so profound, for purposes unknown to him, Marius felt for a moment as if he had stumbled by chance upon some great conspiracy. Yet that could scarcely be, for the people here collected might have figured as the earliest handsel, or pattern, of a new world, from the very face of which discontent had passed away. Corresponding to the variety of human type there present, was the various expression of every form of human sorrow assuaged. What desire, what fulfilment of desire, had wrought so pathetically on the features of these ranks of aged men and women of humble condition? Those young men, bent down so discreetly on the details of their sacred service, had faced life and were glad, by some science, or light of knowledge they had, to which there had certainly been no parallel in the older world. Was some credible message from beyond 'the flaming rampart of the world'—a message of hope regarding the place of men's souls and their interest in the sum of things—already moulding anew their very bodies, and looks, and voices, now and here? At least, there was a cleansing and kindling flame at work in them, which seemed to make everything else Marius had ever known look comparatively vulgar and mean."

The spectacle of the Sacrament adds its deep impression, "bread and wine especially—pure wheaten bread, the pure white wine of the Tusculan vineyards. There was here a veritable consecration, hopeful and animating, of the earth's gifts, of old dead and dark matter itself, now in some way redeemed at last, of all that we can touch and see, in the midst of a jaded world that had lost the true sense of such things."

The sense of youth in it all was perhaps the dominating impression—the youth that was yet old as the world in experience and discovery of the true meaning of life. The young Christ was rejuvenating the world, and all things were being made new by him.

This is the climax of the book. He meets Lucian the aged, who for a moment darkens his dawning faith, but that which has come to him has been no casual emotion, no forced or spectacular conviction. He does not leap to the recognition of Christianity at first sight, but very quietly realises and accepts it as that secret after which his pagan idealism had been all the time groping. The story closes amid scenes of plague and earthquake and martyrdom in which he and Cornelius are taken prisoners, and he dies at last a Christian. "It was the same people who, in the grey, austere evening of that day, took up his remains, and buried them secretly, with their accustomed prayers; but with joy also, holding his death, according to their generous view in this matter, to have been of the nature of a martyrdom; and martyrdom, as the Church had always said, a kind of Sacrament with plenary grace."

Such is some very brief and inadequate conception of one of the most remarkable books of our time, a book "written to illustrate the highest ideal of the æsthetic life, and to prove that beauty may be made the object of the soul in a career as pure, as concentrated, and as austere as any that asceticism inspires. *Marius* is an apology for the highest Epicureanism, and at the same time it is a texture which the author has embroidered with exquisite flowers of imagination, learning, and passion. Modern humanism has produced no more admirable product than this noble dream of a pursuit through life of the spirit of heavenly beauty." Nothing could be more true, so far as it goes, than this admirable paragraph, yet Pater's book is more than that. The main drift of it is the reconciliation of Hellenism with Christianity in the experience of a man "bent on living in the full stream of refined sensation," who finds Christianity in every point fulfilling the ideals of Epicureanism at its best.

The spiritual stages through which Marius passes on his journey towards this goal are most delicately portrayed. In the main these are three, which, though they recur and intertwine in his experience, yet may be fairly stated in their natural order and sequence as normal types of such spiritual progress.

The first of these stages is a certain vague fear of evil, which seems to be conscience hardly aware of itself as such. It is "the sense of some unexplored evil ever dogging his footsteps," which reached its keenest poignancy in a constitutional horror of serpents, but which is a very subtle and undefinable thing, observable rather as an undertone to his consciousness of life than as anything tangible enough to be defined or accounted for by particular causes. On the journey to Rome, the vague misgivings took shape in one definite experience. "From the steep slope a heavy mass of stone was detached, after some whisperings among the trees above his head, and rushing down through the stillness fell to pieces in a cloud of dust across the road just behind him, so that he felt the touch upon his heel." That was sufficient, just then, to rouse out of its hiding-place his old vague fear of evil—of one's "enemies." Such distress was so much a matter of constitution with him, that at times it would seem that the best pleasures of life could but be snatched hastily, in one moment's forgetfulness of its dark besetting influence. A sudden suspicion of hatred against him, of the nearness of enemies, seemed all at once to alter the visible form of things. When tempted by the earth-bound philosophy of the early period of his development, "he hardly knew how strong that old religious sense of responsibility, the conscience, as we call it, still was within him—a body of inward impressions, as real as those so highly valued outward ones—to offend against which, brought with it a strange feeling of disloyalty, as to a person." Later on, when the "acceptance of things" which he found in Marcus Aurelius had offended him, and seemed to mark the Emperor as his inferior, we find that there is "the loyal conscience within him, deciding, judging himself and every one else, with a wonderful sort of authority." This development of conscience from a vague fear of enemies to a definite court of appeal in a man's judgment of life, goes side by side with his approach to Christianity. The pagan idealism of the early days had never been able to cope with that sense of enemies, nor indeed to understand it; but in the light of his growing Christian faith, conscience disentangles itself and becomes clearly defined.

Another element in the spiritual development of Marius is that which may be called his consciousness of an unseen companion. Marius was constitutionally *personel*, and never could be satisfied with the dry light of pure reason, or with any impersonal ideal whatsoever. For him the universe was alive in a very real sense. At first, however, this was the vaguest of sentiments, and it needed much development before it became clear enough to act as one of the actual forces which played upon his life. We first meet with it in connection with the philosophy of Marcus Aurelius and his habit of inward conversation with himself, made possible by means of the *Logos*, "the reasonable spark in man, common to him with the gods." "There could be no inward conversation with oneself such as this, unless there were indeed some one else aware of our actual thoughts and feelings, pleased or displeased at one's disposition of oneself." This, in a dim way, seemed a fundamental necessity of experience—one of those "beliefs, without which life itself must be almost impossible, principles which had their sufficient ground of evidence in that very fact." So far Marcus Aurelius. But the conviction of some august yet friendly companionship in life beyond the veil of things seen, took form for Marius in a way far more picturesque. The passage which describes it is one of the finest in the book, and may be given at length.

"Through a dreamy land he could see himself moving, as if in another life, and like another person, through all his fortunes and misfortunes, passing from point to point, weeping, delighted, escaping from various dangers. That prospect brought him, first of all, an impulse of lively gratitude: it was as if he must look round for some one else to share his joy with: for some one to whom he might tell the thing, for his own relief. Companionship, indeed, familiarity with others, gifted in this way or that, or at least pleasant to him, had been, through one or another long span of it, the chief delight of the journey. And was it only the resultant general sense of such familiarity, diffused through his memory, that in a while suggested the question whether there had not been—besides Flavian, besides Cornelius even, and amid the solitude which in spite of ardent friendship he had perhaps loved best of all things—some other companion, an unfailing companion, ever at his side throughout; doubling his pleasure in the roses by the way, patient of his peevishness or depression, sympathetic above all with his grateful recognition, onward from his earliest days, of the fact that he was there at all? Must not the whole world around have faded away for him altogether, had he been left for one moment really alone in it?" One can see in this sense of constant companionship the untranslated and indeed the unexamined Christian doctrine of God. And, because this God is responsive to all the many-sided human experience which reveals Him, it will be an actual preparation not for Theism only, but for that complexity in unity known as the Christian Trinity. Nothing could better summarise this whole achievement in religion than Pater's apt sentence, "To have apprehended the *Great Ideal*, so palpably that it defined personal gratitude and the sense of a friendly hand laid upon him amid the shadows of the world."

The third essential development of Marius' thought is that of the City of God, which for him assumes the shape of a perfected and purified Rome, the concrete embodiment of the ideals of life and character. This is indeed the inevitable sequel of any such spiritual developments as the fear of enemies and the sense of an unseen companion. Man moves inevitably to the city, and all his ideals demand an embodiment in social form before they reach their full power and truth. In that house of life which he calls society, he longs to see his noblest dreams find a local habitation and a name. This is the grand ideal passed from hand to hand by the greatest and most outstanding of the world's seers—from Plato to Augustine, from Augustine to Dante—the ideal of the City of God. It is but little developed in the book which we are now considering, for that would be beside the purpose of so intimate and inward a history. Yet we see, as it were, the towers and palaces of this "dear City of Zeus" shining in the clear light of the early Christian time, like the break of day over some vast prospect, with the new City, as it were some celestial new Rome, in the midst of it.

These are but a few glimpses at this very significant and far-reaching book, which indeed takes for its theme the very development from pagan to

Christian idealism with which we are dealing. In it, in countless bright and vivid glances, the beauty of the world is seen with virgin eye. Many phases of that beauty belong to the paganism which surrounds us as we read, yet these are purified from all elements that would make them pagan in the lower sense, and under our eyes they free themselves for spiritual flights which find their resting-place at last and become at once intelligible and permanent in the faith of Jesus Christ.

LECTURE III

THE TWO FAUSTS

IT may seem strange to pass immediately from the time of Marcus Aurelius to Marlowe and Goethe, and yet the tale upon which these two poets wrought is one whose roots are very deep in history, and which revives in a peculiarly vital and interesting fashion the age-long story of man's great conflict. Indeed the saga on which it is founded belongs properly to no one period, but is the tragic drama of humanity. It tells, through all the ages, the tale of the struggle between earth and the spiritual world above it; and the pagan forms which are introduced take us back into the classical mythology, and indeed into still more ancient times.

The hero of the story must be clearly distinguished from Fust the printer, a wealthy goldsmith of Mayence, who, in the middle of the fifteenth century, was partner with Gutenberg in the new enterprise of printing. Robert Browning, in *Fust and his Friends*, tells us, with great vivacity, the story of the monks who tried to exorcise the magic spirits from Fust, but forgot their psalm, and so caused an awkward pause during which Fust retired and brought out a printed copy of the psalm for each of them. The only connection with magic which this Fust had, was that so long as this or any other process was kept secret, it was attributed to supernatural powers.

Faust, although a contemporary of Fust the printer, was a very different character. Unfortunately, our information about him comes almost entirely from his enemies, and their accounts are by no means sparing in abuse. Trithemius, a Benedictine abbot of Spanheim in the early part of the sixteenth century, writes of him with the most virulent contempt, as a debauched person and a criminal whose overweening vanity arrogated to itself the most preposterous supernatural powers. It would appear that he had been some sort of travelling charlatan, whose performing horse and dog were taken for evil spirits, like Esmeralda's goat in Victor Hugo's *Notre Dame.* Even Melanchthon and Luther seem to have shared the common view of him, and at last there was published at Frankfurt the *Historie of the Damnable Life and Deserved Death of Dr. John Faustus.* The date of this work is 1587, and a translation of it appeared in London in 1592. It is a discursive composition, founded upon reminiscences of some ancient stroller who lived very much by his wits; but it took such a hold upon the imagination of the time that, by the latter part of the sixteenth century, Faust had become the necromancer *par excellence.* Into the Faust-book there drifted endless necromantic lore from the Middle Ages and earlier times. It seems to have had some connection with Jewish legends of magicians who invoked the *Satanim,* or lowest grade of elemental spirits not unlike the "elementals" of modern popular spiritualism. It was the story of a Christian selling his soul to the powers of darkness, and it had behind it one of the poems of Hrosvitha of Gandersheim which relates a similar story of an archdeacon of Cilicia of the sixth century, and also the popular tradition of Pope Sylvester the Second, who was suspected of having made the same bargain. Yet, as Lebahn says, "The Faust-legend in its complete form was the creation of orthodox Protestantism. Faust is the foil to Luther, who worsted the Devil with his ink-bottle when he sought to interrupt the sacred work of rendering the Bible into the vulgar tongue." This legend, by the way, is a peculiarly happy one, for Luther not only aimed his ink-bottle at the Devil, but most literally and effectively hit him with it, when he wrote those books that changed the face of religious Europe.

The *Historie* had an immense and immediate popularity, and until well into the nineteenth century it was reproduced and sold throughout Europe. As we read it, we cannot but wonder what manner of man it really was who attracted to himself such age-long hatred and fear, and held the interest of the centuries. In many respects, doubtless, his story was like that of Paracelsus, in whom the world has recognised the struggle of much good with almost inevitable evil, and who, if he had been born in another generation, might have figured as a commanding spiritual or scientific authority.

Christopher Marlowe was born at Canterbury in 1564, two months before Shakespeare. He was the son of a shoemaker, and was the pupil of Kett, a fellow and tutor of Corpus Christi College. This tutor was probably accountable for much in the future Marlowe, for he was a mystic, and was burnt for heresy in 1589. After a short and extremely violent life, the pupil followed his master four years later to the grave, having been killed in a brawl under very disgraceful circumstances. He only lived twenty-nine years, and yet he, along with Kyd, changed the literature of England. Lyly's Pastorals had been the favourite reading of the people until these men came, keen and audacious, to lead and sing their "brief, fiery, tempestuous lives." When they wrote their plays and created their villains, they were not creating so much as remembering. Marlowe's plays were four, and they were all influential. His *Edward the Second* was the precursor of the historical plays of Shakespeare. His other plays were *Tamburlaine the Great*, *Dr. Faustus*, and *The Jew of Malta* (Barabbas). These three were all upon congenial lines, expressing that Titanism in revolt against the universe which was the inspiring spirit of Marlowe. But it was the character of Faust that especially fascinated him, for he found in the ancient magician a pretty clear image of his own desires and ambitions. He was one of those who loved "the dangerous edge of things," and, as Charles Lamb said, "delighted to dally with interdicted subjects." The form of the plays is loose and broken, and yet there is a pervading larger unity, not only of dramatic action, but of spirit. The laughter is loud and coarse, the terror unrelieved, and the splendour dazzling. There is no question as to the greatness of this work as permanent literature. It has long outlived the amazing detractions of Hallam and of Byron, and will certainly be read so long as English is a living tongue.

The next stage in this curious history is a

peculiarly interesting one. In former days there sprang up around every great work of art a forest of slighter literature, in the shape of chap-books, ballads, and puppet plays. By far the most popular of the puppet plays was that founded upon Marlowe's *Faust*. The German version continued to be played in Germany until three hundred years later. Goethe constructed his masterpiece largely by its help. English actors travelling abroad had brought back the story to its native land of Germany, and in every town the bands of strolling players sent Marlowe's great conception far and wide. In England also the puppet play was extremely popular. The drama had moved from the church to the market-place, and much of the Elizabethan drama appeared in this quaint form, played by wooden figures upon diminutive boards. To the modern mind nothing could be more incongruous than the idea of a solemn drama forced to assume a guise so grotesque and childish; but, according to Jusserand, much of the stage-work was extremely ghastly, and no doubt it impressed the multitude. There is even a story of some actors who had gone too far, and into the midst of whose play the real devil suddenly descended with disastrous results. It must, however, be allowed that even the serious plays were not without an abundant element of grotesqueness. The occasion for Faustus' final speech of despair, for instance, was the lowering and raising before his eyes of two or three gilded arm-chairs, representing the thrones in heaven upon which he would never sit. It does not seem to have occurred to the audience as absurd that heaven should be regarded as a kind of drawing-room floating in the air, and indeed that idea is perhaps not yet obsolete. However that may be, it is quite evident that such machinery, ill-suited though it was to the solemnities of tragedy, must have been abundantly employed in the puppet plays.

The German puppet play of *Faust* has been transcribed by Dr. Hamm and translated by Mr. Hedderwick into English. It was obtained at first with great difficulty, for the showmen kept the libretto secret, and could not be induced to lend it. Dr. Hamm, however, followed the play round, listening and committing much of it to memory, and his version was finally completed when his amanuensis obtained for a day or two the original manuscript after plying one of the assistants with much beer and wine. It was a battered book, thumb-marked and soaked with lamp oil, but it has passed on to posterity one of the most remarkable pieces of dramatic work which have come down to us from those times.

In all essentials the play is the same as that of Marlowe, except for the constant interruptions of the clown Casper, who intrudes with his absurdities even into the most sacred parts of the action, and entirely mars the dreadful solemnity of the end by demanding his wages from Faust while the clock is striking the diminishing intervals of the last hour.

It was through this curious intermediary that Goethe went back to Marlowe and created what has been well called "the most mystic poetic work ever created," and "the *Divina Commedia* of the eighteenth century." Goethe's *Faust* is elemental, like *Hamlet*. Readers of *Wilhelm Meister* will remember how profound an impression *Hamlet* had made upon Goethe's mind, and this double connection between Goethe and the English drama forms one of the strongest and most interesting of all the links that bind Germany to England. His *Faust* was the direct utterance of Goethe's own inner life. He says: "The marionette folk of *Faust* murmured with many voices in my soul. I, too, had wandered into every department of knowledge, and had returned early enough, satisfied with the vanity of science. And life, too, I had tried under various aspects, and always came back sorrowing and unsatisfied." Thus *Faust* lay in the depths of Goethe's life as a sort of spiritual pool, mirroring all its incidents and thoughts. The play was begun originally in the period of his *Sturm und Drang*, and it remained unpublished until, in old age, the ripened mind of the great poet took it over practically unchanged, and added the calmer and more intellectual parts. The whole of the Marguerite story belongs to the earlier days.

There is nothing in the whole of literature which could afford us a finer and more fundamental account of the battle between paganism and idealism in the soul of man, than the comparison between the *Fausts* of Marlowe and of Goethe. But before we come to this, it may be interesting to notice two or three points of special interest in the latter drama, which show how entirely pagan are the temptations of Faust.

The first passage to notice is that opening one on Easter Day, where the devil approaches Faust in the form of a dog. Choruses of women, disciples, and angels are everywhere in the air; and although the dog appears first in the open, yet the whole emphasis of the passage is upon the contrast between that brilliant Easter morning with its sunshine and its music, and the close and darkened study into which Faust has shut himself. It is true he goes abroad, but it is not to join with the rest in their rejoicing, but only as a spectator, with all the superiority as well as the wistfulness of his illicit knowledge. Evidently the impression intended is that of the wholesomeness of the crowd and the open air. He who goes in with the rest of men in their sorrow and their rejoicing cannot but find the meaning of Easter morning for himself. It is a festival of earth and the spring, an earth idealised, whose spirit is incarnate in the risen Christ. Faust longs to share in that, and on Easter Eve tries in vain to read his Gospel and to feel its power. But the only cure for such morbid introspectiveness as his, is to cast oneself generously into the common life of man, and the refusal to do this invites the pagan devil.

Another point of interest is the coming of the *Erdgeist* immediately after the *Weltschmerz*. The sorrow that has filled his heart with its melancholy sense of the vanity and nothingness of life, and the thousandfold pity and despondency which go to swell that sad condition, are bound to create a reaction more or less violent towards that sheer worldliness which is the essence of paganism. In Bunyan's *Pilgrim's Progress* it is immediately after his floundering in the Slough of Despond that Christian is accosted by Mr. Worldly Wiseman.

Precisely the same experience is recorded here in Faust, although the story is subtler and more complex than that of Bunyan. The *Erdgeist* which comes to the saddened scholar is a noble spirit, vivifying and creative. It is the world in all its glorious fullness of meaning, quite as true an idealism as that which is expressed in the finest spirit of the Greeks. But for Faust it is too noble. His morbid gloom has enervated him, and the call of the splendid earth is beyond him. So there comes, instead of it, a figure as much poorer than that of Worldly Wiseman as the *Erdgeist* is richer. Wagner represents the poor commonplace world of the wholly unideal. It is infinitely beneath the soul of Faust, and yet for the time it conquers him, being nearer to his mood. Thus Mephistopheles finds his opportunity. The scholar, embittered with the sense that knowledge is denied to him, will take to mere action ; and the action will not be great like that which the *Erdgeist* would have prompted, but poor and unsatisfying to any nobler spirit than that of Wagner.

The third incident which we may quote is that of *Walpurgis-Night*. Some critics would omit this part, which, they say, "has naught of interest in bearing on the main plot of the poem." Nothing could be more mistaken than such a judgment. In the *Walpurgis-Night* we have the play ending in that sheer paganism which is the counterpart to Easter Day at the beginning. Walpurgis has a strange history in German folklore. It is said that Charlemagne, conquering the German forests for the Christian faith, drove before him a horde of recalcitrant pagans, who took a last shelter among the trees of the Brocken. There, on the pagan May-day, in order to celebrate their ancient rites unmolested, they dressed themselves in all manner of fantastic and bestial masks, so as to frighten off the Christianising invaders from the revels. The Walpurgis of *Faust* exhibits paganism at its lowest depths. Sir Mammon is the host who invites his boisterous guests to the riot of his festive night. The witches arrive on broomsticks and pitchforks; singing, not without significance, the warning of woe to all climbers—for here aspiration of any sort is a dangerous crime. The Crane's song reveals the fact that pious men are here, in the Blocksberg, united with devils; introducing the same cynical and desperate disbelief in goodness which Nathaniel Hawthorne has told in similar fashion in his tale of *Young Goodman Brown*; and the most horrible touch of all is introduced when Faust in disgust leaves the revel, because out of the mouth of the witch with whom he had been dancing there had sprung a small red mouse. Throughout the whole play the sense of holy and splendid ideals shines at its brightest in lurid contrast with the hopeless and sordid dark of the pagan earth.

Returning now to our main point, the comparison of Marlowe's play with Goethe's, let us first of all contrast the temptations in the two. Marlowe's play is purely theological. Jusserand finely describes the underlying tragedy of it. "Faust, like Tamburlaine, and like all the heroes of Marlowe, lives in thought, beyond the limit of the possible. He thirsts for a knowledge of the secrets of the universe, as the other thirsted for domination over the world." Both are Titanic figures exactly in the pagan sense, but the form of Faustus' Titanism is the revolt against theology. From the early days of the Christian persecutions, there had been a tendency to divorce the sacred from the secular, and to regard all that was secular as being of the flesh and essentially evil. The mediæval views of celibacy, hermitage, and the monastic life, had intensified this divorce; and while many of the monks were interested in human secular learning, yet there was a feeling, which in many cases became a kind of conscience, that only the divine learning was either legitimate or safe for a man's eternal well-being. The Faust of Marlowe is the Prometheus of his own day. The new knowledge of the Renaissance had spread like fire across Europe, and those who saw in it a resurrection of the older gods and their secrets, unhesitatingly condemned it. The doctrine of immortality had entirely supplanted the old Greek ideal of a complete earthly life for man, and all that was sensuous had come to be regarded as intrinsically sinful. Thus we have for background a divided universe, in which there is a great gulf fixed between this world and the next, and a hopeless cleavage between the life of body and that of spirit.

In this connection we may also consider the women of the two plays. Charles Lamb has asked, "What has Margaret to do with Faust?" and has asserted that she does not belong to the legend at all. Literally, this is true, in so far as there is no Margaret in the earlier form of the play, whose interest was, as we have seen, essentially theological. Yet Margaret belongs to the essential story and cannot be taken out of it. She is the "eternal feminine," in which the battle between the spirit and the flesh, between idealism and paganism, will always make its last stand. Even Marlowe has to introduce a woman. His Helen is, indeed, a mere incident, for the real bride of the soul must be either theological or secular science; and yet so essential and so poignant is the question of woman to the great drama, that the passage in which the incident of Helen is introduced far surpasses anything else in Marlowe's play, and indeed is one of the grandest and most beautiful in all literature.

> "Was this the face that launch'd a thousand ships,
> And burned the topless towers of Iliun?
> Sweet Helen, make me immortal with a kiss.
>
> . . . .
>
> O, thou art fairer than the evening air,
> Clad in the beauty of a thousand stars."

Still, Marlowe's *motif* is not sex but theology. The former heretics whom we named had been saved — Theophilus by the intervention of the Blessed Virgin Mary, and Pope Sylvester snatched from the very jaws of hell—by a return to orthodoxy. That was in the Roman Catholic days, but the savage antithesis between earth and heaven had been taken over by the conscience of Protestantism, making a duality which rendered life always intellectually anxious and almost impossible. It is this condition in which Marlowe finds himself. The good and the evil angels stand to right and left of his Faustus, pleading with him for and against secular science on the one side and theological knowledge on the other. For that is the implication behind the contest between magic and Christianity. "The Faust of the earlier Faust-books and ballads, dramas, puppet shows, which grew out of them, is damned because he prefers the human to the divine knowledge. He laid the Holy

Scriptures behind the door and under the bench, refused to be called Doctor of Theology, but preferred to be called Doctor of Medicine." Obviously here we find ourselves in a very lamentable *cul-de-sac.* Idealism has floated apart from the earth and all its life, and everything else than theology is condemned as paganism.

Goethe changes all that. In the earlier *Weltschmerz* passages some traces of it still linger, where Faust renounces theology; but even there it is not theology alone that he renounces, but philosophy, medicine, and jurisprudence as well, so that his renunciation is entirely different from that of Marlowe's Faustus. In Goethe it is no longer one doctrine or one point of view against another doctrine or another point of view. It is life, vitality in all its forms, against all mere doctrine whatsoever.

> "Grey, dearest friend, is every theory,
> But golden-green is the tree of life."

Thus the times had passed into a sense of the limits of theology such as has been well expressed in Rossetti's lines—

> "Let lore of all theology
> Be to thee all it can be,
> But know,—the power that fashions man
> Measured not out thy little span
> For thee to take the meting-rod
> In turn and so approve on God."

So in Goethe we have the unsatisfied human spirit with its infinite cravings and longings for something more than earth can give—something, however, which is not separated from the earth, and which is entirely different from theological dogma or anything of that sort. In this, Goethe is expressing a constant yearning of his own, which illuminated all his writings like a gentle hidden fire within them, hardly seen in many passages and yet always somehow felt. It is *through* the flesh that he will find the spirit, *through* this world that he will find the next. The quest is ultimately the same as that of Marlowe, but the form of it is absolutely opposed to his. Goethe is as far from Marlowe's theological position as *Peer Gynt* is, and indeed there is a considerable similarity between Ibsen's great play and Goethe's. As the drama develops, it is true that the love of Faust becomes sensual and his curiosity morbid; but the tragedy lies no longer in the belief that sense and curiosity are in themselves wrong, but in the fact that Faust fails to distinguish their high phases from their low. We have already seen that the *Erdgeist* which first appeals to Faust is too great for him, and it is there that the tragedy really lies. The earth is not an accursed place, and the *Erdgeist* may well find its home among the ideals; but Wagner is neither big enough nor clean enough to be man's guide.

The contrast between the high and low ideals comes to its finest and most tragic in the story of Margaret. Spiritual and sensual love alternate through the play. Its tragedy and horror concentrate round the fact that love has followed the lower way. Margaret has little to give to Faust of fellowship along intellectual or spiritual lines. She is a village maiden, and he takes from her merely the obvious and lower kind of love. It is a way which leads ultimately to the dance of the witches and the cellar of Auerbach, yet Faust can never be satisfied with these, and from the witch's mouth comes forth the red mouse—the climax of disgust. In Auerbach's cellar he sees himself as the pagan man in him would like to be. In Martha one sees the pagan counterpart to the pure and simple Margaret, just as Mephistopheles is the pagan counterpart to Faust. The lower forms of life are the only ones in which Martha and Mephistopheles are at home. For Faust and Margaret the lapse into the lower forms brings tragedy. Yet it must be remembered also that Faust and Mephistopheles are really one, for the devil who tempts every man is but himself after all, the animal side of him, the dog.

The women thus stand for the most poignant aspect of man's great temptation. It is not, as we have already said, any longer a conflict between the secular and the sacred that we are watching, nor even the conflict between the flesh and the spirit. It is between a higher and a lower way of treating life, flesh and spirit both. Margaret stands for all the great questions that are addressed to mankind. There are for every man two ways of doing work, of reading a book, of loving a woman. He who keeps his spiritual life pure and high finds that in all these things there is a noble path. He who yields to his lower self will prostitute and degrade them all, and the tragedy that leads on to the mad scene at the close, where the cries of Margaret have no parallel in literature except those of Lady Macbeth, is the inevitable result of choosing the pagan and refusing the ideal. The Blocksberg is the pagan heaven.

A still more striking contrast between the plays meets us when we consider the respective characters of Mephistopheles. When we compare the two devils we are reminded of that most interesting passage in Professor Masson's great essay, which describes the secularisation of Satan between *Paradise Lost* and the *Faust* of Goethe:—

"We shall be on the right track if we suppose Mephistopheles to be what Satan has become after six thousand years. . . . Goethe's Mephistopheles is this same being after the toils and vicissitudes of six thousand years in his new vocation: smaller, meaner, ignobler, but a million times sharper and cleverer. . . . For six thousand years he has been pursuing the walk he struck out at the beginning, plying his self-selected function, dabbling devilishly in human nature, and abjuring all interest in the grander physics; and the consequence is, as he himself anticipated, that his nature, once great and magnificent, has become small, virulent, and shrunken. He, the scheming, enthusiastic Archangel, has been soured and civilised into the clever, cold-hearted Mephistopheles."

Marlowe's devil is of the solemn earlier kind, not yet degraded into the worldling whom Goethe has immortalised. Marlowe's Mephistophilis is essentially the idealist, and it is his Faust who is determined for the world. One feels about Mephistophilis that he is a kind of religious character, although under a cloud. The things he does are done to organ music, and he might be a figure in some stained-glass window of old. Not only is he "a melancholy devil, with a soul above the customary hell," but he actually retains a kind of despairing idealism which somehow ranks him on the side rather of good than of evil. The puppet play curiously emphasises this. "Tell me," says Faust, "what would you do if you could attain to everlasting salvation?" "Hear and despair! Were I to attain to everlasting salvation, I would mount to heaven on a ladder, though every rung were a razor edge." The words are exactly in the spirit of the earlier play. So sad is the devil, so oppressed with a sense of the horror of it all, that, as we read, it almost seems as if Faust were tempting the unwilling Mephistophilis to ruin him.

> "Why, this is hell, nor am I out of it;
> Think'st thou that I, who saw the face of God,
> And tasted the eternal joys of heaven,
> Am not tormented with ten thousand hells
> In being depriv'd of everlasting bliss?
> O Faustus, leave these frivolous demands,
> Which strike a terror to my fainting soul!"

To which Faust replies—

> "What, is great Mephistophilis so passionate
> For being deprivèd of the joys of heaven?
> Learn thou of Faustus manly fortitude,
> And scorn those joys thou never shalt possess."

Goethe's Mephistopheles near the end of the play taunts Faust in the words, "Why dost thou seek our fellowship if thou canst not go through with it? . . . Do we force ourselves on thee, or thou on us?" And one has the feeling that, like most other things the fiend says, it is an apparent truth which is really a lie; but it would have been entirely true if Marlowe's devil had said it.

The Mephistopheles of Goethe is seldom solemnised at all. Once indeed on the Harz Mountains he says—

> "Naught of this genial influence do I know!
> Within me all is wintry.
> . . . .
> How sadly, yonder, with belated glow,
> Rises the ruddy moon's imperfect round!"

Yet there it is merely by discomfort, and not by the pain and hideous sorrow of the world surrounding him, that he is affected. He is like Satan in the Book of Job, except that he is offering his victim luxuries instead of pains. In the prologue in Heaven he speaks with such a jaunty air that Professor Blackie's translation has omitted the passage as irreverent. He is the spirit that *denies*—sceptical and cynical, the anti-Christian that is in us all. His business is to depreciate spiritual values, and to persuade mortals that there is no real distinction between good and bad, or between high and low. We have seen in the character of Cornelius in *Marius the Epicurean* "some inward standard . . . of distinction, selection, refusal, amid the various elements of the period." Here is the extreme opposite. There is no divine discontent in him, nor longing for happier things. He would never have said that he would climb to heaven upon a ladder of razor edges. There is nothing of the fallen angel about him at all, for he is a spirit perfectly content with an intolerable past, present, and future. Before the throne of God he swaggers with the same easy insolence as in Martha's garden. He is the very essence and furthest reach of paganism.

So we have this curious fact, that Marlowe's Faust is the pagan and Mephistophilis the idealist; while Goethe reverses the order, making paganism incarnate in the fiend and idealism in the nobler side of the man. It is a far truer and more natural story of life than that which had suggested it; for in the soul of man there is ever a hunger and thirst for the highest, however much he may abuse his soul. At the worst, there remains always that which "a man may waste, desecrate, never quite lose."

One more contrast marks the difference of the two plays, namely, the fate of Faust. Marlowe's Faust is utterly and irretrievably damned. On the old theory of an essential antagonism between the secular and the sacred, and upon the old cast-iron theology to which the intellect of man was enjoined to conform, there is no escape whatsoever for the rebel. So the play leads on to the sublimely terrific passage at the close, when, with the chiming of the bell, terror grows to madness in the victim's soul, and at last he envies the beasts that perish—

> " For, when they die,
> Their souls are soon dissolved in elements ;
> But mine must live still to be plagued in hell.
> Curs'd be the parents that engender'd me !
> No, Faustus, curse thyself, curse Lucifer
> That hath deprived thee of the joys of heaven."

Goethe, with his changed conception of life in general, could not have accepted this ending. It was indeed Lessing who first pointed out that the final end for Faust must be his salvation and not his doom ; but Goethe must necessarily have arrived at the same conclusion even if Lessing had not asserted it. It is clearly visible throughout the play, by touches here and there, that Faust is not "wholly damnable" as Martha is. His pity for women, relevant to the main plot of the play, breaks forth in horror when he discovers the fate of Margaret. "The misery of this one pierces me to the very marrow, and harrows up my soul ; thou art grinning calmly over the doom of thousands!" And these words follow immediately after an outbreak of blind rage called forth by Mephistopheles' famous words, "She is not the first." Such a Faust as this, we feel, can no more be ultimately lost than can the Mephistophilis of Marlowe. As for Marlowe's Faust, the plea for his destruction is the great delusion of a hard theology, and the only really damnable person in the whole company is the Mephistopheles of Goethe, who seems from first to last continually to be committing the sin against the Holy Ghost.

The salvation of Faust is implicit in the whole structure and meaning of the play. It is worked out mystically in the Second Part, along lines of human life and spiritual interest far-flung into the sphere that surrounds the story of the First. But even in the First Part, the happy issue is involved in the terms of Faust's compact with the devil. Only on the condition that Mephistopheles shall be able to satisfy Faust and cheat him "into self-complacent pride, or sweet enjoyment," only

> "If ever to the passing hour I say,
> So beautiful thou art! thy flight delay"—

only then shall his soul become the prey of the tempter. But from the first, in the scorn of Faust for this poor fiend and all he has to bestow, we read the failure of the plot. Faust may sign a hundred such bonds in his blood with little fear. He knows well enough that a spirit such as his can never be satisfied with what the fiend has to give, nor lie down in sleek contentment to enjoy the earth without afterthought.

It is the strenuous and insatiable spirit of the man that saves him. It is true that "man errs so long as he is striving," but the great word of the play is just this, that no such errors can ever be final. The deadly error is that of those who have ceased to strive, and who have complacently settled down in the acceptance of the lower life with its gratifications and delights.

But such striving is, as Robert Browning tells us in *Rabbi ben Ezra* and *The Statue and the Bust*, the critical and all-important point in human character and destiny. It is this which distinguishes pagan from idealist in the end. Faust's errors fall off from him like a discarded robe; the essential man has never ceased to strive. He has gone indeed to hell, but he has never made his bed there. He is saved by want of satisfaction.

LECTURE IV

CELTIC REVIVALS OF PAGANISM

Omar Kayyám and Fiona Macleod

It is extremely difficult to judge justly and without prejudice the literature of one's own time. So many different elements are pouring into it that it assumes a composite character, far beyond the power of definition or even of epigram to describe as a whole. But, while this is true, it is nevertheless possible to select from this vast amalgam certain particular elements, and to examine them and judge them fairly.

The field in which we are now wandering may be properly included under the head of ancient literature, although in another sense it is the most modern of all. The two authors whom we shall consider in this lecture, although they have come into our literature but recently, yet represent very ancient thought. There is nothing whatsoever that is modern about them. They describe bed-rock human passions and longings, sorrowings and consolations. Each may be claimed as a revival of ancient paganism, but only one of them is capable of translation into a useful idealism.

OMAR KAYYÁM

In the twelfth century, at Khorassán in Persia, Omar Kayyám the poet was born. He lived and died at Naishápúr, following the trade of a tent-maker, acquiring knowledge of every available kind, but with astronomy for his special study. His famous poem, the *Rubáiyát,* was first seen by Fitzgerald in 1856 and published in 1868. So great was the sensation produced in England by the innovating sage, that in 1895 the Omar Kayyám Club was founded by Professor Clodd, and that club has since come to be considered "the blue ribbon of literary associations."

In Omar's time Persian poetry was in the hands of the Súfis, or religious teachers of Persia. He found them writing verses which professed to be mystical and spiritual, but which might sometimes be suspected of earthlier meanings lurking beneath the pantheistic veil. It was against the poetry of such Súfis that Omar Kayyám rose in revolt. Loving frankness and truth, he threw all disguises aside, and became the exponent of materialistic epicureanism naked and unashamed.

A fair specimen of the finest Súfi poetry is *The*

Rose Garden of Sa'di, which it may be convenient to quote because of its easy accessibility in English translation. Sa'di also was a twelfth-century poet, although of a later time than Omar. He was a student of the College in Baghdad, and he lived as a hermit for sixty years in Shiraz, singing of love and war. His mind is full of mysticism, wisdom and beauty going hand in hand through a dim twilight land. Dominating all his thought is the primary conviction that the soul is essentially part of God, and will return to God again, and meanwhile is always revealing, in mysterious hints and half-conscious visions, its divine source and destiny. Here and there you will find the deep fatalism of the East, as in the lines—

> "Fate will not alter for a thousand sighs,
> Nor prayers importunate, nor hopeless cries.
> The guardian of the store-house of the wind
> Cares nothing if the widow's lantern dies."

These, however, are relieved by that which makes a friend of fate—

> "To God's beloved even the dark hour
> Shines as the morning glory after rain.
> Except by Allah's grace thou hast no power
> Nor strength of arm such rapture to attain."

It was against this sort of poetry that Omar Kayyám revolted. He had not any proof of such spiritual assurances, and he did not want that of which he had no proof. He understood the material world around him, both in its joy and sorrow, and emphatically he did not understand any other world. He became a sort of Marlowe's Faust before his time, and protested against the vague spirituality of the Súfis by an assertion of what may be called a brilliant animalism. He loved beauty as much as they did, and there is an oriental splendour about all his work, albeit an earthly splendour. He became, accordingly, an audacious epicurean who "failed to find any world but this," and set himself to make the best of what he found. His was not an exorbitant ambition nor a fiery passion of any kind. The bitterness and cynicism of it all remind us of the inscription upon Sardanapalus' tomb—"Eat, drink, play, the rest is not worth the snap of a finger." Drinking-cups have been discovered with such inscriptions on them—"The future is utterly useless, make the most of to-day,"—and Omar's poetry is full both of the cups and the inscription.

The French interpreter, Nicolas, has indeed spiritualised his work. In his view, when Omar raves about wine, he really means God; when he speaks of love, he means the soul, and so on. As a matter of fact, no man has ever written a plainer record of what he means, or has left his meaning less ambiguous. When he says wine and love he means wine and love—earthly things, which may or may not have their spiritual counterparts, but which at least have given no sign of them to him. The same persistent note is heard in all his verses. It is the grape, and wine, and fair women, and books, that make up the sum total of life for Omar as he knows it.

> "Come, fill the Cup, and in the fire of Spring
> Your Winter-garment of Repentance fling:
> The Bird of Time has but a little way
> To flutter—and the Bird is on the Wing.
>
> A Book of verses underneath the Bough,
> A jug of Wine, a Loaf of Bread—and Thou
> Beside me singing in the Wilderness—
> Oh, Wilderness were Paradise enow!
>
> We are no other than a moving row
> Of Magic Shadow-shapes that come and go
> Round with the sun-illumined Lantern held
> In Midnight by the Master of the Show."

It would show a sad lack of humour if we were to take this too seriously, and shake our heads over our eastern visitor. The cult of Omar has been blamed for paganising English society. Really it came in as a foreign curiosity, and, for the most part, that it has remained. When we had a visit some years ago from that great oriental potentate Li Hung Chang, we all put on our best clothes and went out to welcome him. That was all right so long as we did not naturalise him, a course which neither he nor we thought of our adopting. Had we naturalised him, it would have been a different matter, and even Mayfair might have found the fashions of China somewhat *risqüé*. One remembers that introductory note to Browning's *Ferishtah's Fancies*—"You, Sir, I entertain you for one of my Hundred; only, I do not like the fashion of your garments: you will say they are Persian; but let them be changed."[1] The only safe way of dealing with Omar Kayyám is to insist that his garments be *not* changed. If you naturalise him he will become deadly in the West. The East thrives upon fatalism, and there is a glamour about its most materialistic writings, through which far spiritual things seem to quiver as in a sun-haze. The atmosphere of the West is different, and fatalism, adopted by its more practical mind, is sheer suicide.

Not that there is much likelihood of a nation with the history and the literature of England behind it, ever becoming to any great extent materialistic in the crude sense of Omar's poetry. The danger is subtler. The motto, "Let us eat and drink for to-morrow we die," is capable of spiritualisation, and if you spiritualise that motto it becomes poisonous indeed. For there are various ways of eating and drinking, and many who would not be tempted with the grosser appetites may become pagans by devoting themselves

[1] *King Lear*, Act III. scene vi.

to a rarer banquet, the feast of reason and the flow of soul. It is possible in that way also to take the present moment for Eternity, to live and think without horizons. Mr. Peyton has said, "You see in some little house a picture of a cottage on a moor, and you wonder why these people, living, perhaps, in the heart of a great city, and in the most commonplace of houses, put such a picture there. The reason for it is, that that cottage is for them the signal of the immortal life of men, and the moor has infinite horizons." That is the root of the matter after all—the soul and horizons. He who says, "To-day shall suffice for me," whether it be in the high intellectual plane or in the low earthly one, has fallen into the grip of the world that passeth away; and that is a danger which Omar's advent has certainly not lessened.

The second reason for care in this neighbourhood is that epicureanism is only safe for those whose tastes lie in the direction of the simple life. Montaigne has wisely said that it is pernicious to those who have a natural tendency to vice. But vice is not a thing which any man loves for its own sake, until his nature has suffered a long process of degradation. It is simply the last result of a habit of luxurious self-indulgence; and the temptation to the self-indulgent, the present world in one form or another, comes upon everybody at times.

There are moods when all of us want to break away from the simple life, and feel the splendour of the dazzling lights and the intoxication of the strange scents of the world. To surrender to these has always been, and always will be, deadly. It is the old temptation to cease to strive, which we have already found to be the keynote of Goethe's *Faust.* Kingsley, in one of the most remarkable passages of *Westward Ho!* describes two of Amyas Leigh's companions, settled down in a luscious paradise of earthly delights, while their comrades endured the never-ending hardships of the march. By the sight of that soft luxury Amyas was tempted of the devil. But as he gazed, a black jaguar sprang from the cliff above, and fastened on the fair form of the bride of one of the recreants. "O Lord Jesus," said Amyas to himself, "Thou hast answered the devil for me!"

It does not, however, need the advent of the jaguar to introduce the element of sheer tragedy into luxurious life. In his *Conspiracy of Pontiac,* Parkman tells with rare eloquence the character of the Ojibwa Indians: "In the calm days of summer, the Ojibwa fisherman pushes out his birch canoe upon the great inland ocean of the North; . . . or he lifts his canoe from the sandy beach, and, while his camp-fire crackles on the grass-plot, reclines beneath the trees, and smokes and laughs away the sultry hours, in a lazy luxury of enjoyment. . . . But when winter descends upon the North, sealing up the fountains . . . now the hunter can fight no more against the nipping cold and blinding sleet. Stiff and stark, with haggard cheek and shrivelled lip, he lies among the snowdrifts; till, with tooth and claw, the famished wildcat strives in vain to pierce the frigid marble of his limbs."

Meredith tells of a bird, playing with a magic ring, and all the time trying to sing its song; but the ring falls and has to be picked up again, and the song is broken. It is a good parable of life, that impossible compromise between the magic ring and the simple song. Those who choose the earth-magic of Omar's epicureanism will find that the song of the spirit is broken, until they cease from the vain attempt at singing and fall into an earth-bound silence.

Thus Omar Kayyám has brought us a rich treasure from the East, of splendid diction and much delightful and fascinating sweetness of poetry. All such gifts are an enrichment to the language and a decoration to the thought of a people. When, however, they are taken more seriously, they may certainly bring plague with them, as other Eastern things have sometimes done.

FIONA MACLEOD

To turn suddenly from this curious Persian life and thought to the still more curious life and thought of ancient Scotland is indeed a violent change. Nothing could be more dissimilar than the two types of paganism out of which they spring; and if Fiona Macleod's work may have its dangers for the precarious faith of modern days, they are certainly dangers which attack the soul in a different fashion from those of Omar.

The revelation of Fiona Macleod's identity with William Sharp came upon the English-reading world as a complete surprise. Few deaths have been more lamented in the literary world than his, and that for many reasons. His biography is one of the most fascinating that could be imagined. His personality was a singularly attractive one,—so vital, so indefatigable,—with interests so many-sided, and a heart so sound in all of them. It is characteristic of him that in his young days he ran away for a time with gipsies, for he tells us, "I suppose I was a gipsy once, and before that a wild man of the woods." The two great influences of his life were Shelley and D. G. Rossetti. The story of his literary struggles is brimful of courage and romance, and the impression of the book is mainly that of ubiquity. His insatiable curiosity seems to have led him to know everybody, and every place, and everything.

At length Fiona Macleod was born. She arose out of nowhere, so far as the reading public could discover. Really there was a hidden shy self in Sharp, which must find expression impossible except in some secret way. We knew him as the brilliant critic, the man of affairs, and the wide and experienced traveller. We did not know him, until we discovered that he was Fiona, in that second life of his in the borderland where flesh and spirit meet.

First there came *Pharais* in 1893, and that was the beginning of much. Then came *The Children of To-morrow*, the forerunner of Fiona Macleod. It was his first prose expression of the subjective side of his nature, together with the element of revolt against conventionalities, which was always strongly characteristic of him. It introduced England to the hidden places of the Green Life.

The secret of his double personality was confided only to a few friends, and was remarkably well kept. When pressed by adventurous questioners, some of these allies gave answers which might have served for models in the art of diplomacy. So Sharp wrote on, openly as William Sharp, and secretly as Fiona Macleod. Letters had to reach Fiona somehow, and so it was given out that she was his cousin, and that letters sent to him would be safely passed on to her. If, however, it was difficult to keep the secret from the public, it was still more difficult for one man to maintain two distinct personalities. William Sharp of course had to live, while Fiona might die any day. Her life entailed upon him another burden, not of personification only, but of subject and research, and he was driven to sore passes to keep both himself and her alive. For each was truly alive and individual—two distinct people, one of whom thought of the other as if she were "asleep in another room." Even the double correspondence was a severe burden and strain, for Fiona Macleod had her own large post-bag which had to be answered, just as William Sharp had his. But far beyond any such outward expressions of themselves as these, the difficulty of the double personality lay in deep springs of character and of taste. Sharp's mind was keenly intellectual, observant, and reasoning; while Fiona Macleod was the intuitional and spiritual dreamer. She was indeed the expression of the womanly element in Sharp. This element certainly dominated him, or rather perhaps he was one of those who have successfully invaded the realm of alien sex. In his earlier work, such as *The Lady of the Sea*,—"the woman who is in the heart of woman,"—we have proof of this; for in that especially he so "identified himself with woman's life, seeing it through her own eyes, that he seems to forget sometimes that he is not she." So much was this the case that Fiona Macleod actually received at least one proposal of marriage. It was answered quite kindly, Fiona replying that she had other things to do, and could not think of it; but the little incident shows how true the saying about Sharp was, that "he was always in love with something or another." This loving and love-inspiring element in him has been strongly challenged, and some of the women who have judged him, have strenuously disowned him as an exponent of their sex. Yet the fact is unquestionable that he was able to identify himself in a quite extraordinary degree with what he took to be the feminine soul.

It seems to have something to do with the Celtic genius. One can always understand a Scottish Celt better by comparing him with an Irish one or a Welsh; and it will certainly prove illuminative in the present case to remember Mr. W. B. Yeats while one is thinking of Fiona Macleod. To the present writer it seems that the woman-soul is apparent in both, and that she is singing the same tune; the only difference being, as it were, in the quality of the voice, Fiona Macleod singing in high soprano, and

Mr. Yeats in deep and most heart-searching contralto.

The Fiona Macleod side of Sharp never throve well in London. Hers was the fate of those who in this busy world have retained the faculty and the need for dreaming. So Sharp had to get away from London—driven of the spirit into the wilderness—that his other self might live and breathe. One feels the power of this second self especially in certain words that recur over and over again, until the reader is almost hypnotised by their lilting, and finds himself in a kind of sleep. That dreaming personality, with eyes half closed and poppy-decorated hair, could never live in the bondage of the city cage. The spirit must get free, and the longing for such freedom has been well called "a barbaric passion, a nostalgia for the life of the moor and windy sea."

There are two ways of loving and understanding nature. Meredith speaks of those who only see nature by looking at it along the barrel of a gun. The phrase describes that large company of people who feel the call of the wild indeed, and long for the country at certain seasons, but must always be doing something with nature—either hunting, or camping out, or peradventure going upon a journey like Baal in the Old Testament. But there is another way, to which Carlyle calls attention as characteristic of Robert Burns, and which he pronounces the test of a true poet. The test is, whether he can wander the whole day beside a burn "and no' think lang." Such was Fiona's way with nature. She needed nothing to interest her but the green earth itself, and its winds and its waters. It was surely the Fiona side of Sharp that made him kiss the grassy turf and then scatter it to the east and west and north and south; or lie down at night upon the ground that he might see the intricate patterns of the moonlight, filtering through the branches of the trees.

In all this, it is needless to say, Mr. Yeats offers a close parallel. He understands so perfectly the wild life, that one knows at once that it is in him, like a fire in his blood. Take this for instance—

> "They found a man running there;
> He had ragged long grass-coloured hair;
> He had knees that stuck out of his hose;
> He had puddle water in his shoes;
> He had half a cloak to keep him dry,
> Although he had a squirrel's eye."

Such perfect observation is possible only to the detached spirit, which is indeed doing nothing to nature, but only letting nature do her work. In the sharp outline of this imagery, and in the mind that saw and the heart that felt it, there is something of the keenness of the squirrel's eye for nature.

Fiona's favourite part of nature is the sea. That great and many-sided wonder, whether with its glare of phosphorescence or the stillness of its dead calm, fascinates the poems of Sharp and lends them its spell. But of the prose of Fiona it may be truly said that everything

> ". . . doth suffer a sea-change,
> Into something rich and strange."

These marvellous lines were never more perfectly illustrated than here. As we read we behold the sea, now crouching like a gigantic tiger, now moaning with some Celtic consciousness of the grim and loathsome treasures in its depths, ever haunted and ever haunting. It is probable that Sharp never wrote anything that had not for his ear an undertone of the ocean. Sitting in London in his room, he heard, on one occasion, the sound of waves so loud that he could not hear his wife knocking at the door. Similarly in Fiona Macleod's writing seas are always rocking and swinging. Gulfs are opening to disclose the green dim mysteries of the deeper depths. The wind is running riot with the surface overhead, and the sea is lord in all its mad glory and wonder and fear.

Mr. Yeats has the same characteristic, but again it is possible to draw a fantastic distinction like that between the soprano and the alto. It is lake water rather than the ocean that sounds the undertone of Mr. Yeats' poetry—

> "I will arise and go now, for always night and day
> I hear lake water lapping with low sounds by the shore;
> While I stand on the roadway, or on the pavement grey,
> I hear it in the deep heart's core."

The oldest sounds in the world, Mr. Yeats tells us, are wind and water and the curlew: and of the curlew he says—

> "O curlew, cry no more in the air,
> Or only to the waters of the West;
> Because your crying brings to my mind
> Passion-dimmed eyes and long heavy hair
> That was shaken out over my breast:
> There is enough evil in the crying of wind."

In all this you hear the crying of the wind and the swiftly borne scream of the curlew on it, and you know that lake water will not be far away. This magic power of bringing busy city people out of all their surroundings into the green heart of the forest and the moorland, and letting them hear the sound of water there, is common to them both.

Fiona Macleod is a lover and worshipper of beauty. Long before her, the Greeks had taught the world their secret, and the sweet spell had penetrated many hearts beyond the pale of Greece. It was Augustine who said, "Late I have loved thee, oh beauty, so old and yet so new, late I have loved thee." And Marius the Epicurean, in

Pater's fine phrase, "was one who was made perfect by love of visible beauty." It is a direct instinct, this bracing and yet intoxicating love of beauty for its own sake. Each nation produces a spiritual type of it, which becomes one of the deepest national characteristics, and the Celtic type is easily distinguished. No Celt ever cared for landscape. "It is loveliness I ask, not lovely things," says Fiona; and it is but a step from this to that abstract mystical and spiritual love of beauty, which is the very soul of the Celtic genius. It expresses itself most directly in colours, and the meaning of them is far more than bright-hued surfaces. The pale green of running water, the purple and pearl-grey of doves, still more the remote and liquid colours of the sky, and the sad-toned or the gay garments of the earth—these are more by far to those who know their value than pigments, however delicate. They are either a sensuous intoxication or else a mystic garment of the spirit. Seumas, the old islander, looking seaward at sunrise, says, "Every morning like this I take my hat off to the beauty of the world." And as we read we think of Mr. Neil Munro's lord of Doom Castle walking uncovered in the night before retiring to his rest, and with tears welling in his eyes exclaiming that the mountains are his evening prayer.

Such mystics as these are in touch with far-off things. Sharp, indeed, was led definitely to follow such leading into regions of spiritualism where not many of his readers will be able or willing to follow him, but Fiona Macleod left the mystery vague. It might easily have defined itself in some sort of pantheistic theory of the universe, but it never did so. "The green fire" is more than the sap which flows through the roots of the trees. It is, as Alfred de Musset has called it, the blood that courses through the veins of God. As we realise the full force of that imaginative phrase, the dark roots of trees instinct with life, and the royal liquor rising to its foam of leaves, we have something very like Fiona's mystic sense of nature. Any extreme moment of human experience will give an interpretation of such symbolism—love or death or the mere springtide of the year.

It is not without significance that Sharp and Mr. Yeats and Mr. Symons all dreamed on the same night the curious dream of a beautiful woman shooting arrows among the stars. All the three had indeed the beautiful woman in the heart of them, and in far-darting thoughts and imaginations she was ever sending arrows among the stars. But Mr. Yeats is calmer and less passionate than Fiona, as though he were crooning a low song all the time, while the silent arrows flash from his bow. Sometimes, indeed, he will blaze forth flaming with passion in showers of light of the green fire. Yet from first to last, there is less of the green fire and more of the poppies in Mr. Yeats, and it is Fiona who shoots most constantly and farthest among the stars.

Haunted, that is the word for this world into which we have entered. The house without its guests would be uninhabitable for such poets as these. The atmosphere is everywhere that of a haunted earth where strange terrors and beauties flit to and fro—phantoms of spectral lives which seem to be looking on while we play out our bustling parts upon the stage. They are separate from the body, these shadows, and belong to some former life. They are an ancestral procession walking ever behind us, and often they are changing the course of our visible adventures by the power of sins and follies that were committed in the dim and remotest past. Certainly the author is, as he says, "Aware of things and living presences hidden from the rest." "The shadows are here." The spirits of the dead and the never born are out and at large. These or others like them were the folk that Abt Vogler encountered as he played upon his instrument—"presences plain in the place."

One of the most striking chapters in that very

remarkable book of Mr. Fielding Hall's, *The Soul of a People*, is that in which he describes the nats, the little dainty spirits that haunt the trees of Burmah. But it is not only the Eastern trees that are haunted, and Sharp is always seeing tree-spirits, and nature-spirits of every kind, and talking with them. Now and again he will give you a natural explanation of them, but that always jars and sounds prosaic. In fact, we do not want it; we prefer the "delicate throbbing things" themselves, to any facts you can give us instead of them, for to those who have heard and seen beyond the veil, they are far more real than any of your mere facts. Here we think of Mr. Yeats again with his cry, "Come into the world again wild bees, wild bees." But he hardly needed to cry upon them, for the wild bees were buzzing in every page he wrote.

A world haunted in this fashion has its sinister side, allied with the decaying corpses deep in the earth. When passion has gone into the world beyond that which eye hath seen and ear heard, it takes, in presence of the thought of death, a double form. It is in love with death and yet it hates death. So we come back to that singular sentence of Robert Louis Stevenson's, "The beauty and the terror of the world," which so adequately describes the double fascination of nature for man. Her spell is both sweet and terrible, and we would not have it otherwise. The menace in summer's beauty, the frightful contrast between the laughing earth and the waiting death, are all felt in the prolonged and deep sense of gloom that broods over much of Fiona's work, and in the second-sight which very weirdly breaks through from time to time, forcing our entrance into the land from which we shrink.

Mr. Yeats is not without the same sinister and moving undergloom, although, on the whole, he is aware of kindlier powers and of a timid affection between men and spirits. He actually addresses a remonstrance to Scotsmen for having soured the disposition of their ghosts and fairies, and his reconstructions of the ancient fairyland are certainly full of lightsome and pleasing passages. Along either lane you may arrive at peace, which is the monopoly neither of the Eastern nor of the Western Celt, but it is a peace never free from a great wistfulness.

> "How many loved your moments of glad grace,
> And loved your beauty with love false or true;
> But one man loved the pilgrim soul in you,
> And loved the sorrows of your changing face."

That there is much paganism in all this must be obvious to any one who has given any attention to the subject. The tale of *The Annir-Choille* confesses it frankly enough, where the young

Christian prince is brought back by the forest maiden from his new faith to the ancient pagan world. Old gods are strewn everywhere upon the waysides down which Fiona leads us, and there are many times when we cannot disentangle the spiritual from the material, nor indeed the good from the evil influences. Dr. John Brown used to tell the story of a shepherd boy near Biggar, who one day was caught out on the hill in a thunder-storm. The boy could not remember whether thunder-storms were sent by God or Satan, and so, to be quite safe, he kept alternately repeating the ejaculations, "Eh, guid God," and "Eh, bonny deil." One often thinks of Fiona in connection with that story. You are seldom quite sure whether it is a Christian or a pagan deity whom you are invoking, but there is no question as to the paganism of the atmosphere which you often breathe.

As a matter of fact, William Sharp began in frank and avowed paganism, and passed from that through various phases into a high spirituality. His early utterances in regard to Art, in which he deprecated any connection between Art and a message, and insisted upon its being mere expression, were of course sheer paganism. In 1892, before Fiona was born, he published one of those delightful magazines which run through a short and daring career and then vanish as suddenly as they arose. In fact his magazine, *The Pagan Review*, from first to last had only one number. It was edited by Mr. Brooks and William Sharp, and its articles were contributed by seven other people. But these seven, and Mr. Brooks as well, turned out eventually all to be William Sharp himself. It was "frankly pagan; pagan in sentiment, pagan in convictions, pagan in outlook. . . . The religion of our forefathers has not only ceased for us personally, but is no longer in any vital and general sense a sovereign power in the realm." He finished up with the interesting phrase, "Sic transit gloria Grundi," and he quotes Gautier: "'Frankly I am in earnest this time. Order me a dove-coloured vest, apple-green trousers, a pouch, a crook; in short, the entire outfit of a Lignon shepherd. I shall have a lamb washed to complete the pastoral. . . .' This is the lamb."

The magazine was an extraordinarily clever production, and the fact that he was its author is significant. For to the end of her days Fiona was a pagan still, albeit sometimes a more or less converted pagan. In *The Annir-Choille, The Sin-Eater, The Washer of the Ford*, and the others, you never get away from the ancient rites, and there is one story which may be taken as typical of all the rest, *The Walker in the Night*:—

"Often he had heard of her. When any man

met this woman his fate depended on whether he saw her before she caught sight of him. If she saw him first, she had but to sing her wild strange song, and he would go to her; and when he was before her, two flames would come out of her eyes, and one flame would burn up his life as though it were dry tinder, and the other would wrap round his soul like a scarlet shawl, and she would take it and live with it in a cavern underground for a year and a day. And on that last day she would let it go, as a hare is let go a furlong beyond a greyhound. Then it would fly like a windy shadow from glade to glade, or from dune to dune, in the vain hope to reach a wayside Calvary: but ever in vain. Sometimes the Holy Tree would almost be reached; then, with a gliding swiftness, like a flood racing down a valley, the Walker in the Night would be alongside the fugitive. Now and again unhappy nightfarers—unhappy they, for sure, for never does weal remain with any one who hears what no human ear should hearken—would be startled by a sudden laughing in the darkness. This was when some such terrible chase had happened, and when the creature of the night had taken the captive soul, in the last moments of the last hour of the last day of its possible redemption, and rent it this way and that, as a hawk scatters the feathered fragments of its mutilated quarry."

We have said that nature may be either an intoxication or a sacrament, and paganism might be defined as the view of nature in the former of these two lights. But where you have a growing spirituality like that of William Sharp, you are constantly made aware of the hieratic or sacramental quality in nature also. It is this which gives its peculiar charm and spell to Celtic folklore in general. The Saxon song of Beowulf is a rare song, and its story is the swinging tale of a "pagan gentleman very much in the rough," but for the most part it is quite destitute of spiritual significance. It may be doubted if this could be said truly of any Celtic tale that was ever told. Fiona Macleod describes *The Three Marvels* as "studies in old religious Celtic sentiment, so far as that can be recreated in a modern heart that feels the same beauty and simplicity in the early Christian faith"; and there is a constant sense that however wild and even wicked the tale may be, yet it has its Christian counterpart, and is in some true sense a strayed idealism.

At this point we become aware of one clear distinction between William Sharp and Fiona Macleod. To him, literature was a craft, laboured at most honestly and enriched with an immense wealth both of knowledge and of cleverness; but to her, literature was a revelation, with divine inspirations behind it—inspirations authentically divine, no matter by what name the God might be called. So it came to pass that *The Pagan Review* had only one number. That marked the transition moment, when Fiona Macleod began to predominate over William Sharp, until finally she controlled and radically changed him into her own likeness. He passes on to the volume entitled *The Divine Adventure*, which interprets the spirit of Columba. Nature and the spiritual meet in the psychic phase into which Sharp passed, not only in the poetic and native sense, but in a more literal sense than that. For the Green Life continually leads those who are akin to it into opportunities of psychical research among obscure and mysterious forces which are yet very potent. With a nature like his it was inevitable that he should be eventually lured irresistibly into the enchanted forest, where spirit is more and more the one certainty of existence.

For most of us there is another guide into the spirit land. In the region of the spectral and occult many of us are puzzled and ill at ease, but we all, in some degree, understand the meaning of ordinary human love. Even the most commonplace nature has its magical hours now and then, or at least has had them and has not forgotten; and it is love that "leads us with a gentle hand into the silent land." This may form a bond of union between Fiona Macleod and many who are mystified rather than enlightened by psychic phenomena in the technical meaning of the phrase. Here, perhaps, we find the key to the double personality which has been so interesting in this whole study. It was William Sharp who chose for his tombstone the inscription, "Love is more great than we conceive, and death is the keeper of unknown redemptions." Fiona's work, too, is full of the latent potency of love. Like Marius, she has perceived an unseen companion walking with men through the gloom and brilliance of the West and North, and sometimes her heart is so full that it cannot find utterance at all. In the "dream state," that which is mere nature for the scientist reveals itself, obscurely indeed and yet insistently, as very God. God is dwelling in Fiona. He is smiling in all sunsets. He is filling the universe with His breath and holding us all in His "Mighty Moulding Hand."

The relation in which all this stands to Christianity is a very curious question. The splendour, beauty, and spirituality of it all are evident enough, but the references to anything like dogmatic or definite Christian doctrine are confusing and obscure. Perhaps it was impossible that one so literally a child of nature, and who had led such an open-air life from his childhood, could possibly have done otherwise than to rebel. It was the gipsy in him that revolted against Christianity and every other form and convention of civilised life, and claimed a freedom far beyond any which he ever used. We read that in his sixth year, when already he found the God of the pulpit remote and forbidding, he was nevertheless conscious of a benign and beautiful presence. On the shore of Loch Long he built a little altar of rough stones beneath a swaying pine, and laid an offering of white flowers upon it. In the college days he turned still more definitely against orthodox Presbyterianism; but he retained all along, not only belief in the central truths that underlie all religions, but great reverence and affection for them.

It is probable that towards the close he was approaching nearer to formal Christianity than he knew. We are told that he "does not reverence the Bible or Christian Theology in themselves, but for the beautiful spirituality which faintly breathes through them like a vague wind blowing through intricate forests." His quarrel with Christianity was that it had never done justice to beauty, that it had a gloom upon it, and an unlovely austerity. This indeed is a strange accusation from so perfect an interpreter of the Celtic gloom as he was, and the retort *tu quoque* is obvious enough. There have indeed been phases of Christianity which seemed to love and honour the ugly for its own sake, yet there is a rarer beauty in the Man of Sorrows than in all the smiling faces of the world. This is that hidden beauty of which the saints and mystics tell us. They have seen it in the face more marred than any man's, and their record is that he who would find a lasting beauty that will satisfy his soul, must find it through pain conquered and ugliness transformed and sorrow assuaged. The Christ Beautiful can never be seen when you have stripped him of the Crown of Thorns, nor is there any loveliness that has not been made perfect by tears. Thus though there is truth in Sharp's complaint that Christianity has often done sore injustice to beauty as such, yet it must be repeated that this exponent of the Celtic heart somehow missed the element in Christianity which was not only like, but actually identical with, his own deepest truth.

Sharp often reminds one of Heine, with his intensely human love of life, both in its brightness and in its darkness. Where that love is so intense as it was in these hearts, it is almost inevitable that it should sometimes eclipse the sense of the divine. Thus Sharp tells us that "Celtic paganism lies profound still beneath the fugitive drift of Christianity and civilisation, as the deep sea beneath the coming and going of the tides." He was indeed so aware of this underlying paganism, that we find it blending with Christian ideas in practically the whole of his work. Nothing could be quoted as a more distinctive note of his genius than that blend. It is seen perhaps most clearly in such stories as *The Last Supper* and *The Fisher of Men.* In these tales of unsurpassable power and beauty, Fiona Macleod has created the Gaelic Christ. The Christ is the same as He of Galilee and of the Upper Room in Jerusalem, and His work the same. But he talks the sweet Celtic language, and not only talks it but *thinks* in it also. He walks among the rowan trees of the Shadowy Glen, while the quiet light flames upon the grass, and the fierce people that lurk in shadow have eyes for the helplessness of the little lad who sees too far. Such tales are full of a strange light that seems to be, at one and the same time, the Celtic glamour and the Light of the World.

All the lovers of Mr. Yeats must have remembered many instances of the same kind in his work. "And are there not moods which need heaven, hell, purgatory, and faeryland for their expression, no less than this dilapidated earth? Nay, are there not moods which shall find no expression unless there be men who dare to mix heaven, hell, purgatory, and faeryland together, or even to set the heads of beasts to the bodies of men, or to thrust the souls of men into the heart of rocks? Let us go forth, the tellers of tales, and seize whatever prey the heart longs for, and have no fear."

Mr. Yeats is continually identifying these apparently unrelated things; and youth and peace, faith and beauty, are ever meeting in converging lines in his work. No song of his has a livelier lilt than the *Fiddler of Dooney*.

> "I passed my brother and cousin:
> They read in their books of prayer;
> I read in my book of songs
> I bought at Sligo fair.
>
> When we come at the end of time,
> To Peter sitting in state,
> He will smile on the three old spirits,
> But call me first through the gate.
>
> And when the folk there spy me,
> They will all come up to me,
> With, 'Here is the fiddler of Dooney!'
> And dance like a wave of the sea."

In a few final words we may try to estimate what all this amounts to in the long battle between paganism and idealism. There is no question that Fiona Macleod may be reasonably claimed by either side. Certainly it is true of her work, that it is pure to the pure and dangerous to those who take it wrongly. Meredith's great line was never truer than it is here, "Enter these enchanted woods, ye who dare." The effect upon the mind, and the tendency in the life, will depend upon what one brings to the reading of it.

All this bringing back of the discarded gods has its glamour and its risk. Such gods are excellent as curiosities, and may provide the quaintest of studies in human nature. They give us priceless fragments of partial and broken truth, and they exhibit cross-sections of the evolution of thought in some of its most charming moments. Besides all this, they are exceedingly valuable as providing us with that general sense of religion, vague and illusive, which is deeper than all dogma.

But, for the unwary, there is the double danger in all this region that they shall, on the one hand, be tempted to worship the old gods; or that, on the other hand, even in loving them without definite worship, the old black magic may spring out upon them. As to the former alternative, light minds will always prefer the wonderfully coloured but more or less formless figure in a dream, to anything more definite and commanding. They will cry, "Here is the great god"; and, intoxicated by the mystery, will fall down to worship. But that which does not command can never save, and for a guiding faith we need something more sure than this.

Moreover, there is the second alternative of the old black magic. A discarded god is always an uncanny thing to take liberties with. While the earth-spirit in all its grandeur may appeal to the jaded and perplexed minds of to-day as a satisfying object of faith, the result will probably be but a modern form of the ancient Baal-worship. It will in some respects be a superior cult to its ancient prototype. Its devotees will not cut themselves with knives. They will cut themselves with sweet and bitter poignancies of laughter and tears, when the sun shines upon wet forests in the green earth. This, too, is Baal-worship, hardly distinguishable in essence from that cruder devotion to the fructifying and terrifying powers of nature against which the prophets of Israel made their war. In much that Fiona Macleod has written we feel the spirit struggling like Samson against its bonds of green withes, though by no means always able to break them as he did; or lying down in an earth-bound stupor, content with the world that nature produces and sustains. Here, among the elemental roots of things, when the heart is satisfying itself with the passionate life of nature, the red flower grows in the green life, and the imperative of passion becomes the final law.

On the other hand, a child of nature may remember that he is also a child of the spirit; and, even in the Vale Perilous, the spirit may be an instinctive and faithful guide. Because we love the woods we need not worship the sacred mistletoe. Because we listen to the sea we need not reject greater and more intelligible voices of the Word of Life. And the mention of the sea, and the memory of all that it has meant in Fiona Macleod's writing, reminds us strangely of that old text, "Born of water and of the Spirit." While man lives upon the sea-girt earth, the voices of the ocean, that seem to come from the depths of its green heart, will always call to him, reminding him of the mysterious powers and the terrible beauties among which his life is cradled. Yet there are deeper secrets which the spirit of man may learn—secrets that will still be told when the day of earth is over, when the sea has ceased from her swinging, and the earth-spirit has fled for ever. It is well that a man should remember this, and remain a spiritual man in spite of every form of seductive paganism.

Sharp has said in his *Green Fire*:—

"There are three races of man. There is the myriad race which loses all, through (not bestiality, for the brute world is clean and sane) perverted animalism; and there is the myriad race which denounces humanity, and pins all its faith and joy to a life the very conditions of whose existence are incompatible with the law to which we are subject; the sole law, the law of nature. Then there is that small untoward class which knows the divine call of the spirit through the brain, and the secret whisper of the soul in the heart, and for ever perceives the veils of mystery and the rainbows of hope upon our human horizons: which hears and sees, and yet turns wisely, meanwhile, to the life of the green earth, of which we are part, to the common kindred of living things, with which we are at one—is content, in a word, to live, because of the dream that makes living so mysteriously sweet and poignant; and to dream, because of the commanding immediacy of life."

There are indeed the three races. There is the pagan, which knows only the fleshly aspect of life, and seeks nothing beyond it. There is the spiritual, which ignores and seeks to flee from that to which its body chains it. There is also that wise race who know that all things are theirs, flesh and spirit both, and who have learned how to reap the harvests both of time and of eternity.

LECTURE V

JOHN BUNYAN

WE have seen the eternal battle in its earlier phases surging to and fro between gods of the earth that are as old as Time, and daring thoughts of men that rose beyond them and claimed a higher inheritance. Between that phase of the warfare and the same battle as it is fought to-day, we shall look at two contemporary men in the latter part of the seventeenth century who may justly be taken as examples of the opposing types. John Bunyan and Samuel Pepys, however, will lead us no dance among the elemental forces of the world. They will rather show us, with very fascinating *naïveté*, true pictures of their own aspirations, nourished in the one case upon the busy and crowded life of the time, and in the other, upon the definite and unquestioned conceptions of a complete and systematic theology. Yet, typical though they are, it is easy to exaggerate their simplicity, and it will be interesting to see how John Bunyan, supposed to be a pure idealist, aloof from the world in which he lived, yet had the most intimate and even literary connection with that world. Pepys had certain curious and characteristic outlets upon the spiritual region, but he seems to have closed them all, and become increasingly a simple devotee of things seen and temporal.

Bunyan comes upon us full grown and mature in the work by which he is best known and remembered. His originality is one of the standing wonders of history. The *Pilgrim's Progress* was written at a time when every man had to take sides in a savage and atrocious ecclesiastical controversy. The absolute judgments passed on either side by the other, the cruelties practised and the dangers run, were such as to lead the reader to expect extreme bitterness and sectarian violence in every religious writing of the time. Bunyan was known to his contemporaries as a religious writer, pure and simple, and a man whose convictions had caused him much suffering at the hands of his enemies. Most of the first readers of the *Pilgrim's Progress* had no thought of any connection between that book and worldly literature; and the pious people who shook their heads over his allegory as being rather too interesting for a treatise on such high themes as those which it handled, might perhaps have shaken their heads still more solemnly had they known how much of what they called the world was actually behind it. Bunyan was a voluminous writer of theological works, and the complete edition of them fills three enormous volumes, closely printed in double column. But it is the little allegory embedded in one of these volumes which has made his fame eternal, and for the most part the rest are remembered now only in so far as they throw light upon that story. One exception must be made in favour of *Grace Abounding*. This is Bunyan's autobiography, in which he describes, without allegory, the course of his spiritual experience. For an understanding of the *Pilgrim's Progress* it is absolutely necessary to know that companion volume.

It is very curious to watch the course of criticism as it was directed to him and to his story. The eighteenth century had lost the keenness of former controversies, and from its classic balcony it looked down upon what seemed to it the somewhat sordid arena of the past. *The Examiner* complains that he never yet knew an author that had not his admirers. Bunyan and Quarles have passed through several editions and pleased as many readers as Dryden and Tillotson. Even

Cowper, timidly appreciative and patronising, wrote of the "ingenious dreamer"—

"I name thee not, lest so despised a name
Should move a sneer at thy deserved fame,"

—lines which have a pathetic irony in them, as we contrast the anxious Cowper, with the occasional revivals of interest and the age-long tone of patronage which have been meted out to him, with the robust and sturdy immortality of the man he shrank from naming. Swift discovered Bunyan's literary power, and later Johnson and Southey did him justice. In the nineteenth century his place was secured for ever, and Macaulay's essay on him will probably retain its interest longer than anything else that Macaulay wrote.

We are apt to think of him as a mere dreamer, spinning his cobwebs of imagination wholly out of his own substance—a pure idealist, whose writing dwells among his ideals in a region ignorant of the earth. In one of his own apologies he tells us, apparently in answer to accusations that had been made against him, that he did not take his work from anybody, but that it came from himself alone. Doubtless that is true so far as the real originality of his work is concerned, its general conception, and the working out of its details point by point. Yet, to imagine that if there had been no other

English literature the *Pilgrim's Progress* would have been exactly what it is, is simply to ignore the facts of the case. John Bunyan is far more interesting just because his work is part of English literature, because it did feel the influences of his own time and of the past, than it could ever have been as the mere monstrosity of detachment which it has been supposed to be. The idealist who merely dreams and takes no part in the battle, refusing to know or utilise the writing of any other man, can be no fair judge of the life which he criticises, and no reliable guide among its facts.

Bunyan might very easily indeed have been a pagan of the most worldly type. It was extremely difficult for him to be a Puritan, not only on account of outward troubles, but also of inward ones belonging to his own disposition and experience. Accepting Puritanism, the easiest course for him would have been that of fanaticism, and had he taken that course he would certainly have had no lack of companions. It was far more difficult to remain a Puritan and yet to keep his heart open to the beauty and fascination of human life. Yet he was interested in what men were writing or had written. All manner of songs and stories, heard in early days in pot-houses, or in later times in prison, kept sounding in his ears, and he wove them into his work. The thing that he meant to say, and did say, was indeed one about which controversy and persecution were raging, but, except in a very few general references, his writing shows no sign of this. His eye is upon far-off things, the things of the soul of man and the life of God, but the way in which he tells these things shows innumerable signs of the bright world of English books.

It is worth while to consider this large and human Bunyan, who has been very erroneously supposed to be a mere literary freak, detached from all such influences as go to the making of other writers. He tells us, indeed, that "when I pulled it came," and that is delightfully true. Yet, it came not out of nowhere, and it is our part in this essay to inquire as to the places from which it did come. As we have said, it came out of two worlds, and the web is most wonderfully woven and coloured, but our present concern is rather with the earthly part of it than the heavenly.

No one can read John Bunyan without thinking of George Herbert. Few of the short biographies in our language are more interesting reading than Isaac Walton's life of Herbert. That master of simplicity is always fascinating, and in this biography he gives us one of the most beautiful sketches of contemporary narrative that has ever been penned. Herbert was the quaintest of the saints. He lived in the days of Charles the First and James the First, a High Churchman who had Laud for his friend. Shy, sensitive, high-bred, shrinking from the world, he was at the same time a man of business, skilful in the management of affairs, and yet a man of morbid delicacy of imagination. The picture of his life at Little Gidding, where he and Mr. Farrer instituted a kind of hermitage, or private chapel of devotion, in which the whole of the Psalms were read through once in every twenty-four hours, grows peculiarly pathetic when we remember that the house and chapel were sacked by the parliamentary army, in which for a time John Bunyan served. No two points of view, it would seem, could be more widely contrasted than those of Bunyan and Herbert, and yet the points of agreement are far more important than the differences between them, and *The Temple* has so much in common with the *Pilgrim's Progress* that one is astonished to find that the likenesses seem to be entirely unconscious. Matthew Henry is perpetually quoting *The Temple* in his Commentary. Writing only a few years earlier, Bunyan reproduces in his own fashion many of its thoughts, but does not mention its existence.

In order to know Bunyan's early life, and indeed to understand the *Pilgrim's Progress* at all adequately, one must read *Grace Abounding*.

It is a short book, written in the years when he was already growing old, for those whom he had brought into the fold of religion. From this autobiography it has usually been supposed that he had led a life of the wildest debauchery before his Christian days; but the more one examines the book, and indeed all his books, the less is one inclined to believe in any such desperate estimate of the sins of his youth. The measure of sin is the sensitiveness of a man's conscience; and where, as in Bunyan's case, the conscience is abnormally delicate and subject to violent reactions, a life which in another man would be a pattern of innocence and respectability may be regarded as an altogether blackguardly and vicious one. It was, however evidently a life of strong and intense worldly interest stepping over the line here and there into positive wrong-doing, but for the most part blameworthy mainly on account of its absorption in the passing shows of the hour.

What then was that world which interested Bunyan so intensely, and cost him so many pangs of conscience? No doubt it was just the life of the road as he travelled about his business; for though by no means a tinker in the modern sense of the word, he was an itinerant brazier, whose business took him constantly to and fro among the many villages of the district of Bedford. He must have heard in inns and from wayside companions many a catch of plays and songs, and listened to many a lively story, or read it in the chap-books which were hawked about the country then. It must also be remembered that these were the days of puppet shows. The English drama, as we have already mentioned in connection with *Faust*, was by no means confined to the boards of actual theatres where living actors played the parts. Little mimic stages travelled about the country in all directions reproducing the plays, very much after the fashion of Punch and Judy; and even the solemnest of Shakespeare's tragedies were exhibited in this way. There is no possibility of doubt that Bunyan must have often stood agape at these exhibitions, and thus have received much of the highest literature at second hand.

As to how much of it he had actually read, that is a different question. One is tempted to believe that he must have read George Herbert, but of this there is no positive proof. We are quite certain about five books, for which we have his own express statements. His wife brought him as her dowry the very modest furniture of two small volumes, Baily's *Practice of Piety* and Dent's *The Plain Man's Pathway to Heaven.* The first is a very complicated and elaborate statement of Christian dogma, which Bunyan passes by with the scant praise, "Wherein I also found some things that were somewhat pleasing to me." The other is a much more vital production. Even to this day it is an immensely interesting piece of reading. It consists of conversations between various men who stand for types of worldling, ignoramus, theologian, etc., and there are very clear traces of it in the *Pilgrim's Progress*, especially in the talks between Bunyan's pilgrims and the man Ignorance.

Another book which played a large part in Bunyan's life was the short biography of Francis Spira, an Italian, who had died shortly before Bunyan's time. Spira had been a Protestant lawyer in Italy, but had found it expedient to abate the open profession of Protestantism with which he began, and eventually to transfer his allegiance to the Roman Church. The biography is for the most part an account of his death-bed conversation, which lasted a long time, since his illness was even more of the mind than of the body. It is an extremely ghastly account of a morbid and insane melancholia. It was the fashion of the time to take such matters spiritually rather than physically, and we read that many persons went to his death-bed and listened to his miserable cries and groanings in the hope of gaining edification for their souls. How the book came into Bunyan's hands no one can tell, but evidently he had found it in English translation, and many of the darkest parts of *Grace Abounding* are directly due to it, while the Man in the Iron Cage quotes the very words of Spira.

Another book which Bunyan had read was Luther's *Commentary on the Galatians.* The present writer possesses a copy of that volume dated 1786, at the close of which there are fourteen pages, on which long lists of names are printed. The names are those of weavers, shoemakers, and all sorts of tradesmen in the western Scottish towns of Kilmarnock, Paisley, and others of that neighbourhood, who had subscribed for a translation of the commentary that they might read it in their own tongue. This curious fact reminds us that the book had among the pious people of our country an audience almost as enthusiastic as Bunyan himself was. Another of his books, and the only one quoted by name in the *Pilgrim's Progress* or *Grace Abounding*, with the exception of Luther on Galatians, is Foxe's *Book of Martyrs*, traces of which are unmistakable in such incidents as the trial and death of Faithful and in other parts.

In these few volumes may be summed up the entire literary knowledge which Bunyan is known to have possessed. He stands apart from mere book-learning, and deals with life rather through his eyes and ears directly than through the medium of books. But then those eyes and ears of his were no ordinary organs; and his imagination, whose servants they were, was quick to enlist every vital and suggestive image and idea for its own uses. Thus the rich store of observation which he had already laid up through the medium of puppet plays, fragments of song and popular story, was all at his disposal when he came to need it. Further, even in his regenerate days, there was no dimming of the imaginative faculty nor of the observant. The whole neighbourhood in which he lived was an open book, in which he read the wonderful story of life in many tragic and comic tales of actual fact; and in the prison where he spent twelve years, he must often have heard from his fellow-prisoners such fragments as they knew and remembered, with which doubtless they would beguile the tedium of their confinement. That would be for the most part in the first and second imprisonments, extending from the years 1660 to 1672. The third imprisonment was a short affair of only some nine months, spent in the little prison upon the bridge of Bedford, where there would be room for very few companions. The modern bridge crosses the river at almost exactly the same spot; and if you look over the parapet you may see, when the river is low, traces of what seem to be the foundations of the old prison bridge.

When we would try to estimate the processes by which the great allegory was built up, the first fact that strikes us is its extreme aloofness from current events which must have been very familiar to him. In others of his works he tells many stories of actual life, but these are of a private and more or less gossiping nature, many of them fantastic and grotesque, such as those appalling tales of swearers, drunkards, and other specially notorious sinners being snatched away by the devil—narratives which bear the marks of crude popular imagination in details like the actual smell of sulphur left behind. In the whole *Pilgrim's Progress* there is no reference whatever to the Civil War, in which we know that Bunyan had fought, although there are certain parts of it which were probably suggested by events of that campaign. The allegory is equally silent concerning the Great Fire and the Great Plague of London, which were both fresh in the memory of every living man. The only phrase which might have been suggested by the Fire, is that in which the Pilgrim says, "I hear that our little city is to be destroyed by fire"—a phrase which obviously has much more direct connection with the destruction of Sodom than with that of London. The only suggestions of those disastrous latter years of the reign of Charles the Second, are some doubtful allusions to the rise and fall of persecution, few of which can be clearly identified with any particular events.

There are several interesting indications that Bunyan made use of recent and contemporary secular literature. The demonology of the *Pilgrim's Progress* is quite different from that of the *Holy War*. It used to be suggested that Bunyan had altered his views in consequence of the publication of Milton's *Paradise Regained*, which appeared in 1671. That was when it was generally supposed that he had written the *Pilgrim's Progress* in his earlier imprisonment. If, as is now conceded, it was in the later imprisonment that he wrote the book, this theory loses much of its plausibility, for Milton published his *Paradise Regained* before the first edition of the *Pilgrim's Progress* was penned. It is, of course, always possible that between the *Pilgrim's Progress* and the *Holy War* Bunyan may have seen Milton's work, or may have been told about it, for he certainly changed his demonology and made it more like Milton's. Again, there are certain passages in Spenser's *Faerie Queene* which bear so close a resemblance to Bunyan's description of the Celestial City, that it is difficult not to suppose that either directly or indirectly that poem had influenced Bunyan's creation; while in at least one of his songs he approaches so near both the language and the rhythm of a song of Shakespeare's as to make it very probable that he had heard it sung.[1]

These suppositions are not meant in any way to detract from the originality of the great allegory, but rather to link the writer in with that English literature of which he is so conspicuous an ornament. They are no more significant and no less, than the fact that so much of the geography of the *Pilgrim's Progress* seems not to have been created by his imagination, but to have been built up from well-remembered landscapes. From his prison window he could not but see the ruins of old Bedford Castle, which stood demolished upon its hill even in his time. This, together with Cainhoe Castle, only a few miles away, may well have suggested the Castle of Despair in Bypath Meadow near the River of God. Again, memories of Elstow play a notable part in the story. A cross stood there, at the foot of which, when he was play-

[1] Compare the song of Mr. Valiant-for-Truth beginning,

"Who would true valour see"

with Shakespeare's

"Who doth ambition shun."

As You Like It, II. v.

ing the game of cat upon a certain Sunday, the voice came to his soul with its tremendous question, "Wilt thou leave thy sins and go to heaven, or have thy sins and go to hell?" There stood the Moot Hall as it stands to-day, in which, during his worldly days, he had danced with the rest of the villagers and gained his personal knowledge of Vanity Fair. There, as he tells us expressly, is the wicket gate, the rough old oak and iron gate of Elstow parish church. Close beside it, just as you read in the story, stands that great tower which suggested a devil's castle beside the wicket gate, whence Satan showered his arrows on those who knocked below. Not only so, but there was a special reason why for Bunyan that ancient church tower may well have been symbolic of the stronghold of the devil; for it had bells in it, and he was so fond of bell-ringing that it got upon his conscience and became his darling sin. It is easy to make light of his heart-searchings about so innocent an employment, but doubtless there were other things that went along with it. We have all seen those large drinking-vessels, known as bell-ringers' jugs; and these perhaps may suggest an explanation of the sense of sin which burdened his conscience so heavily. Anyhow, there the tower stands, and in the Gothic doorway of it there are one or two deeply cut grooves, obviously made by the ropes of the bell-ringers when, instead of standing below their ropes, they preferred the open air, and drew the ropes through the archway of the door, so as to cut into its moulding. The little fact gains much significance in the light of Bunyan's own confession that he was so afraid that the bell would fall upon him and kill him as a punishment from God, that he used to go outside the door to ring it. Then again there was the old convent at Elstow, where, long before Bunyan's time, nuns had lived, who were known to tradition as "the ladies of Elstow." Very aristocratic and very human ladies they seem to have been, given to the entertainment of their friends in the intervals of their tasteful devotion, and occasionally needing a rebuke from headquarters. Yet it seems not improbable that there is some glorified memory of those ladies in the inhabitants of the House Beautiful, which house itself appears to have been modelled upon Houghton House on the Ampthill heights, built by Sir Philip Sidney's sister but a century before. The silver mine of Demas might seem to have come from some far-off source in chap-book or romance, until we remember that at the village of Pulloxhill, which had been the original home of the Bunyan family, and near which Bunyan was arrested and brought for examination to the house of Justice Wingate, there are the actual remains of an ancient gold mine whose tradition still lingers among the villagers.

All these things seem to indicate that the great allegory is by no means so remote from the earth as has sometimes been imagined; and perhaps the most touching commentary upon this statement is the curious and very unlovely burying-ground in Bunhill fields, cut through by a straight path that leads from one busy thoroughfare to another. A few yards to the left of that path is the tomb and monument of John Bunyan, while at an equal distance to the right lies Daniel Defoe. The *Pilgrim's Progress* and *Robinson Crusoe* are perhaps the two best-known stories in the world, and they are not so far remote from one another as they seem.

Nor was it only in the outward material with which he worked that John Bunyan had much in common with the romance and poetry of England. He could indeed write verses which, for sheer doggerel, it would be difficult to match, but in spite of that there was the authentic note of poetry in him. Some of his work is not only vigorous, inspiring, and full of the brisk sense of action, but has an unconscious strength and worthiness of style, whose compression and terseness have fulfilled at least one of the canons of high literature. Take, for example, the lines on Faithful's death—

"Now Faithful, play the man, speak for thy God:
Fear not the wicked's malice, nor their rod:
Speak boldly, man, the truth is on thy side;
Die for it, and to life in triumph ride."

Or take this as a second example, from his *Prison Meditations*—

"Here come the angels, here come saints,
Here comes the Spirit of God,
To comfort us in our restraints
Under the wicked's rod.

This gaol to us is as a hill,
From whence we plainly see
Beyond this world, and take our fill
Of things that lasting be.

We change our drossy dust for gold,
From death to life we fly:
We let go shadows, and take hold
Of immortality."

This whole poem has in it not merely the bright march of a very vigorous mind, but also a great many of the elements which long before had built up the ancient romances. In it, and in much else that he wrote, he finds a congenial escape from the mere middle-class respectability of his time, and ranges himself with the splendid chivalry both of the past and of the present. There is an elfin element in him as there was in Chaucer, which now and again twinkles forth in a quaint touch of humour, or escapes from the merely spiritual into an extremely interesting human region.

In *Grace Abounding* he very pleasantly tells us

that he could have written in a much higher style if he had chosen to do so, but that for our sakes he has refrained. He does, however, sometimes "step into" his finer style. There is some exquisite pre-Raphaelite work that comes unexpectedly upon the reader, in which he is not only a poet, but a writer capable of seeing and of describing the most highly coloured and minute detail: "Besides, on the banks of this river on either side were green trees, that bore all manner of fruit. . . ." "On either side of the river was also a meadow, curiously beautified with lilies; and it was green the year long." At other times he affrights us with a sudden outburst of the most terrifying imagination, as in the close of the poem of *The Fly at the Candle*—

> "At last the Gospel doth become their snare,
> Doth them with burning hands in pieces tear."

His imagination was sometimes as quaint and sweet as at other times it could be lurid and powerful. *Upon a Snail* is not a very promising subject for a poem, but its first lines justify the experiment—

> "She goes but softly, but she goeth sure;
> She stumbles not, as stronger creatures do."

He can adopt the methods of the stately poets of nature, and break into splendid descriptions of natural phenomena—

"Look, look, brave Sol doth peep up from beneath,
Shews us his golden face, doth on us breathe;
Yea, he doth compass us around with glories,
Whilst he ascends up to his highest stories,
Where he his banner over us displays,
And gives us light to see our works and ways."

Again, in the art of childlike interest and simplicity he can write such lines as these—

OF THE CHILD WITH THE BIRD ON THE BUSH

"My little bird, how canst thou sit
  And sing amidst so many thorns?
Let me but hold upon thee get,
  My love with honour thee adorns.

'Tis true it is sunshine to-day,
  To-morrow birds will have a storm;
My pretty one, come thou away,
  My bosom then shall keep thee warm.

My father's palace shall be thine,
  Yea, in it thou shalt sit and sing;
My little bird, if thou'lt be mine,
  The whole year round shall be thy spring.

I'll keep thee safe from cat and cur,
  No manner o' harm shall come to thee:
Yea, I will be thy succourer,
  My bosom shall thy cabin be."

The last line might have been written by Ben Jonson, and the description of sunrise in the former poem might almost have been from Chaucer's pen.

Yet the finest poetry of all is the prose allegory of the *Pilgrim's Progress.* English prose had taken many centuries to form, in the moulding hands of Chaucer, Malory, and Bacon. It had come at last to Bunyan with all its flexibility and force ready to his hand. He wrote with virgin purity, utterly free from mannerisms and affectations; and, without knowing himself for a writer of fine English, produced it.

The material of the allegory also is supplied from ancient sources. One curious paragraph in Bunyan's treatise entitled *Sighs from Hell*, gives us a broad hint of this. "The Scriptures, thought I then, what are they? A dead letter, a little ink and paper, of three or four shillings price. Alack! what is Scripture? Give me a ballad, a news-book, *George on Horseback* or *Bevis of Southampton.* Give me some book that teaches curious Arts, that tells old Fables." In *The Plain Man's Pathway to Heaven* there is a longer list of such romances as these, including *Ellen of Rummin*, and many others. As has been already stated, these tales of ancient folklore would come into his hands either by recitation or in the form of chap-books. The chap-book literature of Old England was most voluminous and interesting. It consisted of romances and songs, sold at country fairs and elsewhere, and the passing reference which we have quoted proves conclusively, what we might have known without any proof, that Bunyan knew them.

George on Horseback has been identified by Professor Firth with the *Seven Champions of England*, an extremely artificial romance, which may be taken as typical of hundreds more of its kind. The 1610 edition of it is a very lively book with a good deal of playing to the gallery, such as this: "As for the name of Queen, I account it a vain title; for I had rather be an English lady than the greatest empress in the world." There is not very much in this romance which Bunyan has appropriated, although there are several interesting correspondences. It is very courtly and conventional. The narrative is broken here and there by lyrics, quite in Bunyan's manner, but it is difficult to imagine Bunyan, with his direct and simple taste, spending much time in reading such sentences as the following: "By the time the purple-spotted morning had parted with her grey, and the sun's bright countenance appeared on the mountain-tops, St. George had rode twenty miles from the Persian Court." On the other hand, when Great-Heart allows Giant Despair to rise after his fall, showing his chivalry in refusing to take advantage of the fallen giant, we remember the incident of Sir Guy and Colebrand in the *Seven Champions*.

> "Good sir, an' it be thy will,
> Give me leave to drink my fill,
> For sweet St. Charity,
> And I will do thee the same deed
> Another time if thou have need,
> I tell thee certainly."

St. George, like Christian in the Valley of the Shadow of Death, traverses an Enchanted Vale, and hears "dismal croakings of night ravens, hissing of serpents, bellowing of bulls, and roaring of monsters."[1] St. Andrew traverses a land of continual darkness, the Vale of Walking Spirits, amid similar sounds of terror, much as the pilgrims of the Second Part of Bunyan's story traverse the Enchanted Ground. And as these pilgrims found deadly arbours in that land, tempting them to repose which must end in death, so St. David was tempted in an Enchanted Garden, and fell flat upon the ground, "when his eyes were so fast locked up by magic art, and his waking senses drowned in such a dead slumber, that it was as impossible to recover himself from sleep as to pull the sun out of the firmament."

Bevis of Southampton has many points in common with St. George in the *Seven Champions*. The description of the giant, the escape of Bevis from his dungeon, and a number of other passages show how much was common stock for the writers of these earlier romances. There is the same rough humour in it from first to last, and the wonderful swing and stride of vigorous rhyming metre. Of the humour, one quotation will be

[1] For these and other points of resemblance, cf. Professor Firth's Leaflet on Bunyan (*English Association Papers*, No. 19).

enough for an example. It is when they are proposing to baptize the monstrous giant at Cologne, whom Bevis had first conquered and then engaged as his body-servant. At the christening of Josian, wife of Bevis, the Bishop sees the giant.

> "'What is,' sayde he, 'this bad vysage?'
> 'Sir,' sayde Bevys, 'he is my page—
> I pray you crysten hym also,
> Thoughe he be bothe black and blo!'
> The Bysshop crystened Josian,
> That was as white as any swan;
> For Ascaparde was made a tonne,
> And whan he shulde therein be done,
> He lept out upon the brenche
> And sayde: 'Churle, wylt thou me drenche?
> The devyl of hel mot fetche the
> I am to moche crystened to be!'
> The folke had gode game and laughe,
> But the Bysshop was wrothe ynoughe."

There is a curious passage which is almost exactly parallel to the account of the fight with Apollyon in the *Pilgrim's Progress*, and which was doubtless in Bunyan's mind when he wrote that admirable battle sketch—

> "Beves is swerde anon upswapte,
> He and the geaunt togedre rapte;
> And delde strokes mani and fale,
> The nombre can i nought telle in tale.
> The geaunt up is clubbe haf,
> And smot to Beves with is staf,
> But his scheld flegh from him thore,
> Three acres brede and somedel more,

Tho was Beves in strong erur
And karf ato the grete levour,
And on the geauntes brest a-wonde
That negh a-felde him to the grounde.
The geaunt thoughte this bataile hard,
Anon he drough to him a dart,
Throgh Beves scholder he hit schet,
The blold ran doun to Beves' fet,
The Beves segh is owene blod
Out of his wit he wex negh wod,
Unto the geaunt ful swithe he ran,
And kedde that he was doughti man,
And smot ato his nekke bon;
The geant fel to grounde anon."

It is part of his general sympathy with the spirit of the romances that Bunyan's giants were always real giants to him, and he evidently enjoyed them for their own sake as literary and imaginative creations, as well as for the sake of any truths which they might be made to enforce. Despair and Slay-Good are distinct to his imagination. His interest remains always twofold. On the one hand there is allegory, and on the other hand there is live tale. Sometimes the allegory breaks through and confuses the tale a little, as when Mercy begs for the great mirror that hangs in the dining-room of the shepherds, and carries it with her through the remainder of her journey. Sometimes the allegory has to stop in order that a sermon may be preached on some particular point of theology, and such sermons are by no means short. Still the story is so true to life that its irresistible simplicity and naturalness carry it on and make it immortal. When we read such a conversation as that between old Honest and Mr. Standfast about Madam Bubble, we feel that the tale has ceased to be an allegory altogether and has become a novel. This is perhaps more noticeable in the Second Part than in the First. The First Part is indeed almost a perfect allegory; although even there, from time to time, the earnestness and rush of the writer's spirit oversteps the bounds of consistency and happily forgets the moral because the story is so interesting, or forgets for a moment the story because the moral is so important. In the Second Part the two characters fall apart more definitely. Now you have delightful pieces of crude human nature, naïve and sparkling. Then you have long and intricate theological treatises. Neither the allegorical nor the narrative unity is preserved to anything like the same extent as on the whole is the case in Part I. The shrewd and humorous touches of human nature are especially interesting. Bunyan was by no means the gentle saint who shrank from strong language. When the gate of Doubting Castle is opening, and at last the pilgrims have all but gone free, we read that "the lock went damnable hard." When Great-Heart is delighted with Mr. Honest, he calls him "a cock of the right kind." The poem

On Christian Behaviour, which we have already quoted, contains the lines—

> "When all men's cards are fully played,
> Whose will abide the light?"

These are quaint instances of the way in which even the questionable parts of the unregenerate life of the dreamer came in the end to serve the uses of his religion.

There are many gems in the Second Part of the *Pilgrim's Progress* which are full of mother-wit and sly fun. Mr. Honest confesses, "I came from the town of Stupidity; it lieth about four degrees beyond the City of Destruction." Then there is Mr. Fearing, that morbidly self-conscious creature, who is so much at home in the Valley of Humiliation that he kneels down and kisses the flowers in its grass. He is a man who can never get rid of himself for a moment, and who bores all the company with his illimitable and anxious introspection. Yet, in Vanity Fair, when practical facts have to be faced instead of morbid fancies and inflamed conscience, he is the most valiant of men, whom they can hardly keep from getting himself killed, and for that matter all the rest of them. Here, again, is an inimitable flash of insight, where Simple, Sloth, and Presumption have prevailed with "one Short-Wind, one Sleepy-Head, and with a young woman, her name was Dull, to turn out of the way and become as they."

Every now and then these natural touches of portraiture rise to a true sublimity, as all writing that is absolutely true to the facts of human nature tends to do. Great-Heart says to Mr. Valiant-for-Truth, "Let me see thy sword," and when he has taken it in his hand and looked at it for awhile, he adds, "Ha! it is a right Jerusalem blade." That sword lingers in Bunyan's imagination, for, at the close of Valiant's life, part of his dying speech is this, "My sword I give to him that shall succeed me in my pilgrimage, and my courage and skill to him that can get it. My marks and scars I carry with me, to be a witness for me that I have fought His battles."

Bunyan is so evidently an idealist and a prince of spiritual men, that no one needs to point out this characteristic of the great dreamer, nor to advertise so obvious a thing as his spiritual idealism. We have accordingly taken that for granted and left it to the reader to recognise in every page for himself. We have sought in this to show what has sometimes been overlooked, how very human the man and his work are. Yet his humanism is ever at the service of the spirit, enlivening his book and inspiring it with a perpetual and delicious interest, but never for a moment entangling him again in the old yoke of bondage, from which at his conversion he had been set free. For the human as opposed to the divine, the fleshly as the rival of the spiritual, he has an open and profound contempt, which he expresses in no measured terms in such passages as that concerning Adam the First and Madam Wanton. These are for him sheer pagans. At the cave, indeed, which his pilgrim visits at the farther end of the Valley of the Shadow of Death, we read that Pope and Pagan dwelt there in old time, but that Pagan has been dead many a day. Yet the pagan spirit lives on in many forms, and finds an abiding place and home in Vanity Fair. As Professor Firth has pointed out, Ben Jonson, in his play *Bartholomew Fair*, had already told the adventures of two Puritans who strayed into the Fair, and who regarded the whole affair as the shop of Satan. There were many other Fairs, such as that of Sturbridge, and the Elstow Fair itself, which was instituted by the nuns on the ground close to their convent, and which is held yearly to the present day. Such Fairs as these have been a source of much temptation and danger to the neighbourhood, and represent in its popular form the whole spirit of paganism at its worst.

All the various elements of Bunyan's world live on in the England of to-day. Thackeray, with a stroke of characteristic genius, has expanded and applied the earlier conception of paganism in his great novel whose title *Vanity Fair* is borrowed from Bunyan. But the main impression of the allegory is the victory of the spiritual at its weakest over the temporal at its mightiest. His descriptions of the supper and bed chamber in the House Beautiful, and of the death of Christiana at the end of the Second Part, are immortal writings, in the most literal sense, amid the shows of time. They have indeed laid hold of immortality not for themselves only, but for the souls of men. Nothing could sum up the whole story of Bunyan better than the legend of his flute told by Mr. S. S. M'Currey in his book of poems entitled *In Keswick Vale.* The story is that in his prison Bunyan took out a bar from one of the chairs in his cell, scooped it hollow, and converted it into a flute, upon which he played sweet music in the dark and solitary hours of the prison evening. The jailers never could find out the source of that music, for when they came to search his cell, the bar was replaced in the chair, and there was no apparent possibility of flute-playing; but when the jailers departed the music would mysteriously recommence. It is very unlikely that this legend is founded upon fact, or indeed that Bunyan was a musician at all (although we do have from his pen one touching and beautiful reference to the finest music in the world being founded upon the bass), but, like his own greater work, the little legend is an allegory. The world for centuries has heard sweet music from Bunyan, and has not known whence it came. It has seemed to most men a miracle, and indeed they were right in counting it so. Yet there was a flute from which that music issued, and the flute was part of the rough furniture of his imprisoned world. He was no scholar, nor delicate man of *belles lettres*, like so many of his contemporaries. He took what came to his hand; and in this lecture we have tried to show how much did come thus to his hand that was rare and serviceable for the purposes of his spirit, and for the expression of high spiritual truth.

LECTURE VI

PEPYS' DIARY

IT is doubtful whether any of Bunyan's contemporaries had so strong a human interest attaching to his person and his work as Samuel Pepys. There is indeed something in common to the two men,—little or nothing of character, but a certain *naïveté* and sincerity of writing, which makes them remind one of each other many times. All the more because of this does the contrast between the spirit of the two force itself upon every reader; and if we should desire to find a typical pagan to match Bunyan's spirituality and idealism, it would be difficult to go past Samuel Pepys.

There were, as everybody knows, two famous diarists of the Restoration period, Pepys and Evelyn. It is interesting to look at the portraits of the two men side by side. Evelyn's face is anxious and austere, suggesting the sort of stuff of which soldiers or saints are made. Pepys is a voluptuous figure, in the style of Charles the

Second, with regular and handsome features below his splendid wig, and eyes that are both keen and heavy, penetrating and luxurious. These two men (who, in the course of their work, had to compare notes on several occasions, and between whom we have the record of more than one meeting) were among the most famous gossips of the world. But Evelyn's gossip is a succession of solemnities compared with the racy scandal, the infantile and insatiable curiosity, and the incredible frankness of the pagan diarist.

Look at his face again, and you will find it impossible not to feel a certain amount of surprise. Of all the unlikely faces with which history has astonished the readers of books, there are none more surprising than those of three contemporaries in the later seventeenth century. Claverhouse, with his powerful character and indomitable will, with his Titanic daring and relentless cruelty, has the face of a singularly beautiful young girl. Judge Jeffreys, whose delight in blood was only equalled by the foulness and extravagance of his profanity, looks in his picture the very type of spiritual wistfulness. Samuel Pepys, whose large oval eyes and clear-cut profile suggest a somewhat voluptuous and very fastidious aristocrat, was really a man of the people, sharp to a miracle in all the detail of the humblest kind of life, and apparently unable to keep from exposing himself to scandal in many sorts of mean and vulgar predicament.

Since the deciphering and publication of his Diary, a great deal has been written concerning it. The best accounts of it are Henry B. Wheatley's *Samuel Pepys and the World he Lived in*, and Robert Louis Stevenson's little essay in his *Short Studies of Men and Books*. The object of the present lecture is not to give any general account of the time and its public events, upon which the Diary touches at a thousand points, but rather to set the spirit of this man in contrast with that of John Bunyan, which we have just considered. The men are very typical, and any adequate conception of the spirit of either will give a true cross-section of the age in which he lived. Pepys, it must be confessed, is much more at home in his times than Bunyan ever could be. One might even say that the times seem to have been designed as a background for the diarist. There is as little of the spirit of a stranger and pilgrim in Pepys, even in his most pathetic hours, as there is in John Bunyan the spirit of a man at home, even in his securest. It was a very pagan time, and Pepys is the pagan *par excellence* of that time, the bright and shining example of the pagan spirit of England.

His lot was cast in high places, to which he rose by dint of great ability and indomitable perseverance in his office. He talks with the King, the Duke of York, the Archbishop, and all the other great folks of the day; and no volume has thrown more light on the character of Charles the Second than his. We see the King at the beginning kissing the Bible, and proclaiming it to be the thing which he loves above all other things. He rises early in the morning, and practises others of the less important virtues. We see him touching all sorts of people for the King's evil, a process in which Pepys is greatly interested at first, but which palls when it has lost its novelty. Similarly, the diarist is greatly excited on the first occasion when he actually hears the King speak, but soon begins to criticise him, finding that he talks very much like other people. He describes the starvation of the fleet, the country sinking to the verge of ruin, and the maudlin scenes of drunkenness at Court, with a minuteness which makes one ashamed even after so long an interval. However revolting or shameful the institution may be, the fact that it is an institution gives it zest for the strange mind of Pepys. He is, however, capable also of moralising. "Oh, that the King would mind his business!" he would exclaim, after having delighted himself and his readers with the most droll accounts of His

Majesty's frivolities. "How wicked a wretch Cromwell was, and yet how much better and safer the country was in his hands than it is now." And often he will end the bewildering account with some such bitter comment as the assertion "that every one about the Court is mad."

In politics he had been a republican in his early days, and when Charles the First's head fell at Whitehall, he had confided to a friend the dangerous remark that if he were to preach a sermon on that event he would choose as his text the words, "The memory of the wicked shall rot." The later turn of events gave him abundant opportunities for repenting of that indiscretion, and he repents at intervals all through his Diary. For now he is a royalist in his politics, having in him not a little of the spirit of the Vicar of Bray, and of Bunyan's Mr. By-ends.

The political references lead him beyond England, and we hear with consternation now and again about the dangerous doings of the Covenanters in Scotland. We hear much also of France and Holland, and still more of Spain. Outside the familiar European lands there is a fringe of curious places like Tangier, which is of great account at that time, and is destined in Pepys' belief to play an immense part in the history of England, and of the more distant

Bombain in India, which he considers to be a place of little account. Here and there the terror of a new Popish plot appears. The kingdom is divided against itself, and the King and the Commons are at drawn battle with the Lords, while every one shapes his views of things according as his party is in or out of power.

Three great historic events are recorded with singular minuteness and interest in the Diary, namely, the Plague, the Dutch War, and the Fire of London.

As to the Plague, we have all the vivid horror of detail with which Defoe has immortalised it, with the additional interest that here no consecutive history is attempted, but simply a record of daily impressions of the streets and houses. On his first sight of the red cross upon a door, the diarist cries out, "Lord, have mercy upon us," in genuine terror and pity. The coachman sickens on his box and cannot drive his horses home. The gallant draws the curtains of a sedan chair to salute some fair lady within, and finds himself face to face with the death-dealing eyes and breath of a plague-stricken patient. Few people move along the streets, and at night the passenger sees and shuns the distant lights of the link-boys guiding the dead to their burial. A cowardly parson flies upon some flimsy excuse from his dangerous post, and makes a weak apology on his first reappearance in the pulpit. Altogether it is a picture unmatched in its broken vivid flashes, in which the cruelty and wildness of desperation mingle with the despairing cry of pity.

The Dutch War was raging then, not on the High Seas only, but at the very gates of England; and Pepys, whose important and responsible position as Clerk of the Acts of the Navy gave him much first-hand information, tells many great stories in his casual way. We hear the guns distinctly and loud, booming at the mouth of the Thames. The press-gang sweeps the streets, and starving women, whose husbands have been taken from them, weep loudly in our ears. Sailors whose wages have not been paid desert their ships, in some cases actually joining the Dutch and fighting against their comrades. One of the finest passages gives a heartrending and yet bracing picture of the times. "About a dozen able, lusty, proper men came to the coach-side with tears in their eyes, and one of them that spoke for the rest began, and said to Sir W. Coventry, 'We are here a dozen of us, that have long known and loved, and served our dead commander, Sir Christopher Mings, and have now done the last office of laying him in the ground. We would be glad we had any other to offer after him, and in revenge of him. All we have is our lives; if you will please to get His Royal Highness to give us a fire-ship among us all, here are a dozen of us, out of all which, choose you one to be commander; and the rest of us, whoever he is, will serve him; and, if possible, do that which shall show our memory of our dead commander, and our revenge.' Sir W. Coventry was herewith much moved, as well as I, who could hardly abstain from weeping, and took their names, and so parted."

Perhaps, however, the finest work of all is found in the descriptions of the Fire of London. From that night when he is awakened by the red glare of the fire in his bedroom window, on through the days and weeks of terror, when no man knew how long he would have a home, we follow by the light of blazing houses the story of much that is best and much that is worst in human nature. The fire, indeed, cleanses the city from the last dregs of the plague which are still lingering there, but it also stirs up the city until its inhabitants present the appearance of ants upon a disturbed ant-hill. And not the least busy among them, continually fussing about in all directions, is the diarist himself, eagerly planning for the preservation of his money, dragging it hither and thither from hiding-place to hiding-place in the city, and finally burying it in bags at dead of night in a garden. Nothing is too small for him to notice.

The scrap of burnt paper blown by the wind to a lady's hand, on which the words are written, "Time is, it is done," is but one of a thousand equally curious details.

His own character, as reflected in the narrative of these events, is often little to his credit, and the frank and unblushing selfishness of his outlook upon things in general is as amusing as it is shameful. And yet, on the other hand, when most men deserted London, Pepys remained in it through the whole dangerous time of the plague, taking his life in his hand and dying daily in his imagination in spite of the quaint precautions against infection which he takes care on every occasion to describe. Through the whole dismal year, with plague and fire raging around him, he sticks to his post and does his work as thoroughly as the disorganised circumstances of his life allow. If we could get back to the point of view of those who thought about Pepys and formed a judgment of him before his Diary had been made public, we should be confronted with the figure of a man as different from the diarist as it is possible for two men to be. His contemporaries took him for a great Englishman, a man who did much for his country, and whose character was a mirror of all the national and patriotic ideals. His public work was by no means unimportant, even in a time so full of dangers and so critical for the destinies of England. Little did the people who loved and hated him in his day and afterwards dream of the contents of that small volume, so carefully written in such an unintelligible cipher, locked nightly with its little key, and hidden in some secure place. When at last the writing was deciphered, there came forth upon us, from the august and honourable state in which the Navy Commissioner had lain so long, this flood of small talk, the greatest curiosity known to English literature. Other men than Pepys have suffered in reputation from the yapping of dogs and the barn-door cackle that attacked their memories. England blushed as she heard the noise when the name of Carlyle became the centre of such commotion. But if Samuel Pepys has suffered in the same way he has no one to thank for it but himself; for, if his own handwriting had not revealed it, no one could possibly have guessed it from the facts of his public career. Yet what a rare show it is, that multitude of queer little human interests that intermingle with the talk about great things! It may have been quite wrong to translate it, and undoubtedly much of it was disreputable enough for any man to write, yet it will never cease to be read; nor will England cease to be glad that it was translated, so long as the charm of history is doubled by touches of strange imagination and confessions of human frailty.

Pepys' connection with literature is that rather of a virtuoso than of a student in the strict sense of the term. He projected a great History of the Navy, which might have immortalised him in a very different fashion from that of the immortality which the Diary has achieved. But his life was crowded with business and its intervals with pleasures. The weakness of his eyes also militated against any serious contribution to literature, and instead of the History, for which he had gathered much material and many manuscripts, he gave us only the little volume entitled *Memoirs of the Navy*, which, however, shows a remarkable grasp of his subject, and of all corresponding affairs, such as could only have been possessed by a man of unusually thorough knowledge of his business. He collected what was for his time a splendid library, consisting of some three thousand volumes, now preserved in his College (Magdalene College, Cambridge), very carefully arranged and catalogued. We read much of this library while it is accumulating—much more about the mahogany cases in which the books were to stand than about the books themselves, or his own reading of them. The details of their arrangement were very dear to his curious mind. He tells us that where the books would not fit exactly to the shelves, but were smaller than the space, he had little gilded stilts made, adjusted to the size of each book, and placed under the volumes, which they lifted to the proper height. Little time can have been left over for the study of at least the stiffer works in that library, although there are many notes which show that he was in some sense a reader, and that books served the same purpose as events and personalities in leading him up and down the byways of what he always found to be a curious and interesting world.

But the immortal part of Pepys is undoubtedly his Diary. Among others of the innumerable curious interests which this man cultivated was that of studying the secret ciphers which had been invented and used by literary people in the past. From his knowledge of these he was enabled to invent a cipher of his own, or rather to adopt one which he altered somewhat to serve his uses. Having found this sufficiently secret code, he was now able to gratify his immense interest in himself and his inordinate personal vanity by writing an intimate narrative of his own life. The Diary covers nine and a half years in all, from January 1660 to May 1669. For nearly a century and a half it lay dead and silent, until Rev. J. Smith, with infinite diligence and pains, discovered the key to it, and wrote his translation. A later translation has been made by Rev. Mynors Bright, which includes some passages by the judgment of the former translator considered unnecessary or inadvisable.

Opinions differ as to the wisdom, and indeed the morality, of forcing upon the public ear the accidentally discovered secrets which a dead man had guarded so carefully. There is, of course, the possibility that, as some think, Pepys desired that posterity should have the complete record in all its frankness and candour. If this be so, one can only say that the wish is evidence of a morbid and unbalanced mind. It seems much more probable that he wrote the Diary for the luxury of reading it to himself, always intending to destroy it before his death. But a piece of work so intimate as this is, in a sense, a living part of the man who creates it, and one can well imagine him putting off the day of its destruction, and grudging that it should perish with all its power of awakening old chords of memory and revitalising buried years. For his own part he was no squeamish moralist and if it were only for his own eyes he would enjoy passages which the more fastidious public might judge differently.

So it comes to pass that this amazing *omnium gatherum* of a book is among the most living of all the gifts of the past to the present, telling everything and telling it irresistibly. His hat falls through a hole, and he writes down all about the incident as faithfully as he describes the palace of the King of France, and the English war with Holland. His nature is amazingly complicated, and yet our judgment of it is simplified by his passion for telling everything, no matter how discreditable or how ignoble the detail may be. He is a great man and a great statesman, and he is the liveliest of our English crickets on the hearth. One set of excerpts would present him as the basest, another set as the pleasantest and kindliest of men; and always without any exception he is refreshing by his intense and genial interest in the facts of the world. Of the many summaries of himself which he has given us, none is more characteristic than the following, with which he closes the month of April of the year 1666: "Thus ends this month; my wife in the country, myself full of pleasure and expence; in some trouble for my friends, and my Lord Sandwich, by the Parliament, and more for my eyes, which are daily worse and worse, that I dare not write or read almost anything." He is essentially a virtuoso who has been forced by circumstances into the necessity of being also a public man, and has developed on his own account an extraordinary passion for the observation of small and wayside things. At the high table of those times, where Milton and Bunyan sit at the mighty feast of English literature, he is present also: but he is under the table, a mischievous and yet observant child, loosening the neckerchiefs of those who are too drunk, and picking up scraps of conversation which he will retail outside. There is something peculiarly pathetic in the whole picture. One remembers Defoe, who for so many years lived in the reputation of honourable politics and in the odour of such sanctity as Robinson Crusoe could give, until the discovery of certain yellow papers revealed the base political treachery for which the great island story had been a kind of anodyne to conscience. So Samuel Pepys would have passed for a great naval authority and an anxious friend of England when her foes were those of her own household, had he only been able to make up his mind to destroy these little manuscript volumes.

Why did he write them, one still asks? Readers of Robert Browning's poems, *House* and *Shop*, will remember the scorn which that poet pours upon any one who unlocks his heart to the general public. And these narrations of Pepys' are certainly of such a kind that if he intended them to be read by any public in any generation of England, he must be set down as unique among sane men. Stevenson indeed considers that there was in the Diary a side glance at publication, but the proof which he adduces from the text does not seem sufficient to sustain so remarkable a freak of human nature, nor does the fact that on one occasion Pepys set about destroying all his papers except the Diary, appear to prove very much one way or another. Stevenson calls it inconsistent and unreasonable in a man to write such a book and to preserve it unless he wanted it to be read. But perhaps no writing of diaries is quite reasonable; and as for his desire to have it read by others than himself, we find that his Diary was so close a secret that he expresses regret for having mentioned it to Sir William Coventry. No other man ever heard of it in Pepys' lifetime, "it not being necessary, nor maybe convenient, to have it known."

Why, then, did he write it? Why does anybody write a diary? Probably the answer nearest to the truth will be that every one finds himself interesting, and some people have so keen an interest in themselves that it becomes a passion, clamorous to be gratified. Now as Bacon tells us, "Writing maketh an exact man," and the writing of diaries reduces to the keenest vividness our own impressions of experience and thoughts about things. Pepys was, above all other men, interested in himself. He was intensely in love with himself.

The beautiful, jealous, troublesome, and yet inevitable Mrs. Pepys was but second in her husband's affections after all. He was his own wife. One remembers fashionable novels of the time of *Evelina* or the *Mysteries of Udolpho,* and recollects how the ladies there speak lover-like of their diaries, and, when writing them, feel themselves always in the best possible company. For Pepys, his Diary does not seem to have been so much a refuge from daily cares and worries, nor a preparation for the luxury of reading it in his old age, as an indulgence of intense and poignant pleasure in the hour of writing.

His interest in himself was quite extraordinary. When his library was collected and his books bound and gilded they were doubtless a treasured possession of which he was hugely proud. But this was not so much a possession as it was a kind of *alter ego,* a fragment of his living self, hidden away from all eyes but his own. No trifle in his life is too small for record. He cannot change his seat in the office from one side of the fireplace to another without recording it. The gnats trouble him at an inn in the country. His wig takes fire and crackles, and he is mighty merry about it until he discovers that it is his own wig that is burning and not somebody else's. He visits the ships, and, remembering former days, notes down without a blush the sentence, "Poor ship, that I have been twice merry in." Any one could have written the Diary, so far as intellectual or even literary power is concerned, though perhaps few would have chosen precisely Pepys' grammar in which to express themselves. But nobody else that ever lived could have written it with such sheer abandonment and frankness. He has a positive talent, nay, a genius for self-revelation, for there must be a touch of genius in any man who is able to be absolutely true. Other men have struggled hard to gain sincerity, and when it is gained the struggle has made it too conscious to be perfectly sincere. Pepys, with utter unconsciousness, is sincere even in his insincerities. Some of us do not know ourselves and our real motives well enough to attempt any formal statement of them. Others of us may suspect ourselves, but would die before we would confess our real motives even to ourselves, and would fiercely deny them if any other person accused us of them. But this man's barriers are all down. There is no reserve, but frankness everywhere and to an unlimited extent. There is no pose in the book either of good or bad, and it is one of the very few books of which such a statement could be made. He has been accused of many things, but never of affectation. The bad actions are qualified by regrets, and the disarmed critic feels that they have lost any element of tragedy which they might otherwise have had. The good actions are usually spoiled by some selfish *addendum* which explains and at the same time debases them. Surely the man who could do all this constantly through so many hundreds of pages, must be in his way a unique kind of genius, to have so clear an eye and so little self-deception.

The Diary is full of details, for he is the most curious man in the world. One might apply to him the word catholicity if it were not far too big and dignified an epithet. The catholicity of his mind is that of the *Old Curiosity Shop*. The interest of the book is inexhaustible, because to him the whole world was just such a book. His world was indeed

> So full of a number of things
> He was sure we should all be as happy as kings.

Like Chaucer's Pardoner he was "meddlesome as a fly." Now he lights upon a dane's skin hung in a church. Again, upon a magic-lantern. Yet again upon a traitor's head, and the prospect of London in the distance. He will drink four pints of Epsom water. He will learn to whistle like a bird, and he will tell you a tale of a boy who was disinherited because he crowed like a cock. He will walk across half the country to see anything new. His heart is full of a great love of processions, raree-shows of every kind, and, above all, novelty. His confession that the sight of the King touching for the evil gave him no pleasure because he had seen it before, applies to most things in his life. For such a man, this world must indeed have been an interesting place.

We join him in well-nigh every meal he sits down to, from the first days when they lived so plainly, on to the greater times of the end, when he gives a dinner to his friends, which was "a better dinner than they understood or deserved." He delights in all the detail of the table. The cook-maid, whose wages were £4 per annum, had no easy task to satisfy her fastidious master, and Mrs. Pepys must now and then rise at four in the morning to make mince-pies. Any new kind of meat or drink especially delights him. He finds ortolans to be composed of nothing but fat, and he often seems, in his thoughts on other nations, to have for his first point of view the sight of foreigners at dinner. But this is only part of the insatiable and omnivorous interest in odds and ends which is everywhere apparent. The ribbons he has seen at a wedding, the starving seamen who are becoming a danger to the nation, the drinking of wine with a toad in the glass, a lightning flash that melted fetters from the limbs of slaves, Harry's chair (the latest curiosity of the drawing-rooms, whose arms rise and clasp you into it when you sit down), the new Messiah, who comes with a brazier of hot coals and proclaims the doom of England—these, and a thousand other details, make up the furniture of this most miscellaneous mind.

Everything in the world amuses him, and from first to last there is an immense amount of travelling, both physical and mental. With him we wander among companies of ladies and gentlemen walking in gardens, or are rowed up and down the Thames in boats, and it is always exciting and delightful. That is a kind of allegory of the man's view of life. But nothing is quite so congenial to him, after all, as plays at the theatre. One feels that he would never have been out of theatres had it been possible, and in order to keep himself to his business he has to make frequent vows (which are generally more or less broken) that he will not go to see a play again until such and such a time. When the vow is broken and the play is past he lamentably regrets the waste of resolution, and stays away for a time until the next outburst comes. The plays were then held in the middle of the day, and must have cut in considerably upon the working-time of business men; although, to be sure, the office hours began with earliest morning, and by the afternoon things were growing slacker. The light, however, was artificial, and the flare of the candles often hurt his eyes, and gave him a sufficient physical reason to fortify his moral ones for abstention. His taste in the dramatic art would commend itself to few moderns. He has no patience with Shakespeare, and speaks disparagingly of *Twelfth Night*, *Midsummer Night's Dream*, and *Othello*; while he constantly informs us that he "never saw anything so good in his life" as the now long-forgotten productions of little playwrights of his time. He would, we suspect, prefer at all times a puppet show to a play; partly, no doubt, because that was the fashion, and partly because that type of drama was nearer his size. Throughout the volumes of the Diary there are few things of which he speaks with franker and more enthusiastic delight than the enjoyment which he derives from punchinello.

Next to the delight which he derived from the theatre must be mentioned that which he continually found in music. He seems to have made an expert and scientific study of it, and the reader hears continually the sound of lutes, harpsichords, violas, theorbos, virginals, and flageolets. He takes great numbers of music lessons, but quarrels with his teacher from time to time. He praises extravagantly such music as he hears, or criticises it unsparingly, passing on one occasion the desperate censure "that Mrs. Turner sings worse than my wife."

His interest in science is as curious and miscellaneous as his interest in everything else. He was indeed President of the Royal Society of his time, and he is immensely delighted with Boyle and his new discoveries concerning colours and hydrostatics. Yet so rare a dilettante is he, in this as in other things, that we find this President of the Royal Society bringing in a man to teach him the multiplication table. He has no great head for figures, and we find him listening to long lectures upon abstruse financial questions, not unlike the bimetallism discussions of our own day, which he finds so clear, while he is listening, that nothing could be clearer, but half an hour afterwards he does not know anything whatever about the subject.

Under the category of his amusements, physic must be included; for, like other egoists, he was immensely interested in his real or imaginary ailments, and in the means which were taken to cure them. On some days he will sit all day long taking physic. He derives an immense amount of amusement from the process of doctoring himself, and still more from writing down in all their detail both his symptoms and their treatment. His pharmacopœia is by no means scientific, for he includes within it charms which will cure one of anything, and he always keeps a hare's foot by him, and will sometimes tell of troubles which came to him because he had forgotten it.

He is constantly passing the shrewdest of judgments upon men and things, or retailing them from the lips of others. "Sir Ellis Layton is, for a speech of forty words, the wittiest man that ever I knew in my life, but longer he is nothing." "Mighty merry to see how plainly my Lord and Povy do abuse one another about their accounts, each thinking the other a fool, and I thinking they were not either of them, in that point, much in the wrong." "How little merit do prevail in the world, but only favour; and that, for myself, chance without merit brought me in; and that diligence only keeps me so, and will, living as I do among so many lazy people that the diligent man becomes necessary, that they cannot do anything without him." "To the Cocke-pitt where I hear the Duke of Albemarle's chaplain make a simple sermon: among other things, reproaching the imperfection of humane learning, he cried, 'All our physicians cannot tell what an ague is, and all our arithmetique is not able to number the days of a man'—which, God knows, is not the fault of arithmetique, but that our understandings reach not the thing." "The blockhead Albemarle hath strange luck to be loved, though he be, and every man must know it, the heaviest man in the world, but stout and honest to his country." "He advises me in what I write to him, to be as short as I can, and obscure." "But he do tell me that the House is in such a condition that nobody can tell what to make of them, and, he thinks, they were never in before; that everybody leads and nobody follows." "My Lord Middleton did come to-day, and seems to me but a dull, heavy man; but he is a great soldier, and stout, and a needy Lord." A man who goes about the world making remarks of that kind, would need a cipher in which to write them down. His world is everything to him, and he certainly makes the most of it so far as observation and remark are concerned.

If Pepys' curiosity and infinitely varied shrewdness and observation may be justly regarded as phenomenal, the complexity of his moral character is no less amazing. He is full of industry and ambition, reading for his favourite book Bacon's *Faber Fortunæ*, "which I can never read too often." He is "joyful beyond myself that I cannot express it, to see, that as I do take pains, so God blesses me, and has sent me masters that do observe that I take pains." Again he is "busy till night blessing myself mightily to see what a deal of business goes off a man's hands when he stays at it." Colonel Birch tells him "that he knows him to be a man of the old way of taking pains."

This is interesting in itself, and it is a very marked trait in his character, but it gains a wonderful pathos when we remember that this infinite taking of pains was done in a losing battle with blindness. There is a constantly increasing succession of references in the Diary to his failing eyesight and his fears of blindness in the future. The references are made in a matter-of-fact tone, and are as free from self-pity as if he were merely recording the weather or the date. All the more on that account, the days when he is weary and almost blind with writing and reading, and the long nights when he is unable to read, show him to be a very brave and patient man. He consults Boyle as to spectacles, but fears that he will have to leave off his Diary, since the cipher begins to hurt his eyes. The lights of the theatre become intolerable, and even reading is a very trying ordeal, notwithstanding the paper tubes through which he looks at the print, and which afford him much interest and amusement. So the Diary goes on to its pathetic close:—"And thus ends all that I doubt I shall ever be able to do with my own eyes in the keeping of my Journal, I being not able to do it any longer, having done now so long as to undo my eyes almost every time that I take a pen in my hand; and, therefore, whatever comes of it, I must forbear; and, therefore, resolve, from this time forward, to have it kept by my people in long-hand, and must be contented to set down no more than is fit for them and all the world to know; or, if there be anything, I must endeavour to keep a margin in my book open, to add, here and there, a note in shorthand with my own hand.

"And so I betake myself to that course, which is almost as much as to see myself go into my grave; for which, and all the discomforts that will accompany my being blind, the good God prepare me!—S. P."

It is comforting to know that, in spite of these fears, he did not grow blind, but preserved a certain measure of sight to the end of his career.

In regard to money and accounts, his character and conduct present the same extraordinary mixture as is seen in everything else that concerns him. Money flows profusely upon valentines, gloves, books, and every sort of thing conceivable; yet he grudges the price of his wife's dress although it is a sum much smaller than the cost of his own. He allows her £30 for all expenses of the household, and she is immensely pleased, for the sum is much larger than she had expected. The gift to her of a necklace worth £60 overtops all other generosity, and impresses himself so much that we hear of it till we are tired. A man in such a position as his, is bound to make large contributions to public objects, both in the forms of donations and of loans; but caution tempers his public spirit. A characteristic incident is that in which he records his genuine shame that the Navy Board had not lent any money towards the expenses caused by the Fire and the Dutch War. But when the loan is resolved upon, he tells us, with delicious naïveté, how he rushes in to begin the list, lest some of his fellows should head it with a larger sum, which he would have to equal if he came after them. He hates gambling,—it was perhaps the one vice which never tempted him,—and he records, conscientiously and very frequently, the gradual growth of his estate from nothing at all to thousands of pounds, with constant thanks to God, and many very quaint little confessions and remarks.

He was on the one hand confessedly a coward, and on the other hand a man of the most hasty and violent temper. Yet none of his readers can despise him very bitterly for either of these vices. For he disarms all criticism by the incredibly ingenious frankness of his confessions; and the instances of these somewhat contemptible vices alternate with bits of real gallantry and fineness, told in the same perfectly natural and unconscious way.

His relations with his wife and other ladies would fill a volume in themselves. It would not be a particularly edifying volume, but it certainly would be without parallel in the literature of this or any other country for sheer extremity of frankness. Mrs. Pepys appears to have been a very beautiful and an extremely difficult lady, disagreeable enough to tempt him into many indiscretions, and yet so virtuous as to fill his heart with remorse for all his failings, and still more with vexation for her discoveries of them. But below all this surface play of pretty disreputable outward conduct, there seems to have been a deep and genuine love for her in his heart. He can say as coarse a thing about her as has probably ever been recorded, but he balances it with abundance of solicitous and often ineffective attempts to gratify her capricious and imperious little humours.

These curious mixtures of character, however, are but byplay compared with the phenomenal and central vanity, which alternately amazes and delights us. After all the centuries there is a positive charm about this grown man who, after all, never seems to have grown up into manhood. He is as delighted with himself as if he were new, and as interested in himself as if he had been born yesterday. He prefers always to talk with persons of quality if he can find them.

"Mighty glad I was of the good fortune to visit him (Sir W. Coventry), for it keeps in my acquaintance with him, and the world sees it, and reckons my interest accordingly." His public life was distinguished by one great speech made in answer to the accusations of some who had attacked him and the Navy Board in the House of Commons. That speech seems certainly to have been distinguished and extraordinarily able, but it certainly would have cost him his soul if he had not already lost that in other ways. Every sentence of flattery, even to the point of being told that he is another Cicero, he not only takes seriously, but duly records.

There is an immense amount of snobbery, blatant and unashamed. A certain Captain Cooke turns out to be a man who had been very great in former days. Pepys had carried clothes to him when he was a little insignificant boy serving in his father's workshop. Now Captain Cooke's fortunes are reversed, and Pepys tells us of his many and careful attempts to avoid him, and laments his failure in such attempts. He hates being seen on the shady side of any street of life, and is particularly sensitive to such company as might seem ridiculous or beneath his dignity. His brother faints one day while walking with him in the street, on which his remark is, "turned my head, and he was fallen down all along upon the ground dead, which did put me into a great fright; and, to see my brotherly love! I did presently lift him up from the ground." This last sentence is so delightful that, were it not for the rest of the Diary, it would be quite incredible in any human being past the age of short frocks. All this side of his character culminates in the immense amount of information which we have concerning his coach. He has great searching of heart as to whether it would be good policy or bad to purchase it. All that is within him longs to have a coach of his own, but, on the other hand, he fears the jealousy of his rivals and the increased demands upon his generosity which such a luxury may be expected to bring. At last he can resist no longer, and the coach is purchased. No sooner does he get inside it than he assumes the air of a gentleman whose ancestors have ridden in coaches since the beginning of time. "The Park full of coaches, but dusty, and windy, and cold, and now and then a little dribbling of rain; and what made it worse, there were so many hackney coaches as spoiled the sight of the gentlemen's."

A somewhat amazing fact in this strange and contradictory character is the constant element of subtlety which blends with so much frankness. He wants to do wrong in many different ways but he wants still more to do it with propriety, and to have some sort of plausible excuse which will explain it in a respectable light. Nor is it only other people whom he is bent on deceiving. Were that all, we should have a very simple type of hypocritical scoundrel, which would be as different as possible from the extraordinary Pepys. There is a sense of propriety in him, and a conscience of obeying the letter of the law and keeping up appearances even in his own eyes. If he can persuade himself that he has done that, all things are open to him. He will receive a bribe, but it must be given in such a way that he can satisfy his conscience with ingenious words. The envelope has coins in it, but then he opens it behind his back and the coins fall out upon the floor. He has only picked them up when he found them there, and can defy the world to accuse him of having received any coins in the envelope. That was the sort of conscience which he had, and whose verdicts he never seems seriously to have questioned. He vows he will drink no wine till Christmas, but is delighted to find that hippocras, being a mixture of two wines, is not necessarily included in his vow. He vows he will not go to the play until Christmas, but then he borrows money from another man and goes with the borrowed money; or goes to a new playhouse which was not open when the vow was made. He buys books which no decent man would own to having bought, but then he excuses himself on the plea that he has only read them and has not put them in his library. Thus, along the whole course of his life, he cheats himself continually. He prefers the way of honour if it be consistent with a sufficient number of other preferences, and yet practises a multitude of curiously ingenious methods of being excusably dishonourable. On the whole, in regard to public business and matters of which society takes note, he keeps his conduct surprisingly correct, but all the time he is remembering, not without gusto, what he might be doing if he were a knave. It is a curious question what idea of God can be entertained by a man who plays tricks with himself in this fashion. Of Pepys certainly it cannot be said that God "is not in all his thoughts," for the name and the remembrance are constantly recurring. Yet God seems to occupy a quite hermetically sealed compartment of the universe; for His servant in London shamelessly goes on with the game he is playing, and appears to take a pride in the very conscience he systematically hoodwinks.

It is peculiarly interesting to remember that Samuel Pepys and John Bunyan were contemporaries. There is, as we said, much in common between them, and still more in violent contrast. He had never heard of the Tinker or his Allegory so far as his Diary tells us, nor is it likely that he would greatly have appreciated the *Pilgrim's Progress* if it had come into his hands. Even *Hudibras* he bought because it was the proper thing to do, and because he had met its author, Butler; but he never could see what it was that made that book so popular. Bunyan and Pepys were two absolutely sincere men. They were sincere in opposite ways and in diametrically opposite camps, but it was their sincerity, the frank and natural statement of what they had to say, that gave its chief value to the work of each of them. It is interesting to remember that Pepys was sent to prison just when Bunyan came out of it, in the year 1678. The charge against the diarist was indeed a false one, and his imprisonment cast no slur upon his public record: while Bunyan's charge was so true that he neither denied it nor would give any promise not to repeat the offence. Pepys, had he known of Bunyan, would probably have approved of him, for he enthusiastically admired people who were living for conscience' sake, like Dr. Johnson's friend, Dr. Campbell, of whom it was said he never entered a church, but always took off his hat when he passed one. On the whole Pepys' references to the Fanatiques, as he calls them, are not only fair but favourable. He is greatly interested in their zeal, and impatient with the stupidity and brutality of their persecutors.

In regard to outward details there are many interesting little points of contact between the Diary and the *Pilgrim's Progress.* We hear of Pepys purchasing Foxe's *Book of Martyrs*; Bartholomew and Sturbridge Fairs come in for their own share of notice; nor is there wanting a description of such a cage as Christian and Faithful were condemned to in Vanity Fair. Justice Keelynge, the judge who condemned Bunyan, is mentioned on several occasions by Pepys, very considerably to his disadvantage. But by far the most interesting point that the two have in common is found in that passage which is certainly the gem of the whole Diary. Bunyan, in the second part of the *Pilgrim's Progress,* introduces a shepherd boy who sings very sweetly upon the Delectable Mountains. It is the most beautiful and idyllic passage in the whole allegory, and has become classical in English literature. Yet Pepys' passage will match it for simple beauty. He rises with his wife a little before four in the morning to make ready for a journey into the country in the neighbourhood of Epsom. There, as they walk upon the Downs, they come "where a flock of sheep was; and the most pleasant and innocent sight that ever I saw in my life. We found a shepherd and his little boy reading, far from any houses or sight of people, the Bible to him; so I made the boy read to me, which he did. . . . He did content himself mightily in my liking his boy's reading, and did bless God for him, the most like one of the old patriarchs that ever I saw in my life, and it brought those thoughts of the old age of the world in my mind for two or three days after."

Such is some slight conception, gathered from a few of many thousands of quaint and sparkling revelations of this strange character. Over against the "ingenious dreamer," Bunyan, here is a man who never dreams. He is the realist, pure and unsophisticated; and the stray touches of pathos, on which here and there one chances in his Diary, are written without the slightest attempt at sentiment, or any other thought than that they are plain matters of fact. He might have stood for this prototype of many of Bunyan's characters. Now he is Mr. Worldly Wiseman, now Mr. By-ends, and Mr. Hold-the-World; and taken altogether, with all his good and bad qualities, he is a fairly typical citizen of Vanity Fair.

There are indeed in his character exits towards idealism and possibilities of it, but their promise is never fulfilled. There is, for instance, his kindly good-nature. That quality was the one and all-atoning virtue of the times of Charles the Second, and it was supposed to cover a multitude of sins. Yet Charles the Second's was a reign of constant persecution, and of unspeakable selfishness in high places. Pepys persecutes nobody, and yet some touch of unblushing selfishness mars every kindly thing he does. If he sends a haunch of venison to his mother, he lets you know that it was far too bad for his own table. He loves his father with what is obviously a quite genuine affection, but in his references to him there is generally a significant remembrance of himself. He tells us that his father is a man "who, besides that he is my father, and a man that loves me, and hath ever done so, is also, at this day, one of the most careful and innocent men of the world." He advises his father "to good husbandry and to be living within the bounds of £50 a year, and all in such kind words, as not only made both them but myself to weep." He hopes that his father may recover from his illness, "for I would fain do all I can, that I may have him live, and take pleasure in my doing well in the world." Similarly, when his uncle is dying, we have a note "that he is very ill, and so God's Will be done." When the uncle is dead, Pepys' remark is, "sorry in one respect, glad in my expectations in another respect." When his predecessor dies, he writes, "Mr. Barlow is dead; for which God knows my heart, I could be as sorry as is possible for one to be for a stranger, by whose death he gets £100 per annum."

Another exit towards idealism of the Christian and spiritual sort might be supposed to be found in his abundant and indeed perpetual references to churches and sermons. He is an indomitable sermon taster and critic. But his criticisms, although they are among the most amusing of all his notes, soon lead us to surrender any expectation of escape from paganism along this line. "We got places, and staid to hear a sermon; but it, being a Presbyterian one, it was so long, that after above an hour of it we went away, and I home, and dined; and then my wife and I by water to the Opera." This is not, perhaps, surprising, and may in some measure explain his satisfaction with Dr. Creeton's "most admirable, good, learned, and most severe sermon, yet comicall," in which the preacher "railed bitterly ever and anon against John Calvin, and his brood, the Presbyterians," and ripped up Hugh Peters' preaching, calling him "the execrable skellum." One man preaches "well and neatly"; another "in a devout manner, not elegant nor very persuasive, but seems to mean well, and that he would preach holily"; while Mr. Mills makes "an unnecessary sermon upon Original Sin, neither understood by himself nor the people." On the whole, his opinion of the Church is not particularly high, and he seems to share the view of the Confessor of the Marquis de Caranen, "that the three great trades of the world are, the lawyers, who govern the world; the Churchmen who enjoy the world; and a sort of fellows whom they call soldiers, who make it their work to defend the world."

It must be confessed that, when there were pretty ladies present and when his wife was absent, the sermons had but little chance. "To Westminster to the parish church, and there did entertain myself with my perspective glass up and down the church, by which I had the great pleasure of seeing and gazing at a great many very fine women; and what with that, and sleeping, I passed away the time till sermon was done." Sometimes he goes further, as at St. Dunstan's, where "I heard an able sermon of the minister of the place; and stood by a pretty, modest maid, whom I did labour to take by the hand; but she would not, but got further and further from me; and, at last, I could perceive her to take pins out of her pocket to prick me if I should touch her again—which, seeing, I did forbear, and was glad I did spy her design."

He visits cathedrals, and tries to be impressed by them, but more interesting things are again at hand. At Rochester, "had no mind to stay there, but rather to our inne, the White Hart, where we drank." At Canterbury he views the Minster and the remains of Beckett's tomb, but adds, "A good handsome wench I kissed, the first that I have seen a great while." There is something ludicrously incongruous about the idea of Samuel Pepys in a cathedral, just as there is about his presence in the Great Plague and Fire. Among any of these grand phenomena he is altogether out of scale. He is a fly in a thunderstorm.

His religious life and thought are an amazing complication. He can lament the decay of piety with the most sanctimonious. He remembers God continually, and thanks and praises Him for each benefit as it comes, with evident honesty and refreshing gratitude. He signs and seals his last will and testament, "which is to my mind, and I hope to the liking of God Almighty." But in all this there is a curious consciousness, as of one playing to a gallery of unseen witnesses, human or celestial. On a fast-day evening he sings in the garden "till my wife put me in mind of its being a fast-day; and so I was sorry for it, and stopped, and home to cards." He does not indeed appear to regard religion as a matter merely for sickness and deathbeds. When he hears that the Prince, when in apprehension of death, is troubled, but when told that he will recover, is merry and swears and laughs and curses like a man in health, he is shocked. Pepys' religion is the same in prosperous and adverse hours, a thing constantly in remembrance, and whose demands a gentleman can easily satisfy. But his conscience is of that sort which requires an audience, visible or invisible. He hates dissimulation in other people, but he himself is acting all the time. "But, good God! what an age is this, and what a world is this! that a man cannot live without playing the knave and dissimulation."

Thus his religion gave him no escape from the world. He was a man wholly governed by self-interest and the verdict of society, and his religion was simply the celestial version of these motives. He has conscience enough to restrain him from damaging excesses, and to keep him within the limits of the petty vices and paying virtues of a comfortable man—a conscience which is a cross between cowardice and prudence. We are constantly asking why he restrained himself so much as he did. It seems as if it would have been so easy for him simply to do the things which he unblushingly confesses he would like to do. It is a question to which there is no answer, either in his case or in any other man's. Why are all of us the very complex and unaccountable characters that we are?

Pepys was a pagan man in a pagan time, if ever there was such a man. The deepest secret of him is his intense vitality. Here, on the earth, he is thoroughly alive, and puts his whole heart into most of his actions. He is always in the superlative mood, finding things either the best or the worst that "he ever saw in all his life." His great concern is to be merry, and he never outgrows the crudest phases of this desire, but carries the monkey tricks of a boy into mature age. He will draw his merriment from any source. He finds it "very pleasant to hear how the old cavaliers talk and swear." At the Blue Ball, "we to dancing, and then to a supper of French dishes, which yet did not please me, and then to dance and sing; and mighty merry we were till about eleven or twelve at night, with mighty great content in all my company, and I did, as I love to do, enjoy myself." "This day my wife made it appear to me that my late entertainment of this week cost me above £12, an expence which I am almost ashamed of, though it is but once in a great while, and is the end for which, in the most part, we live, to have such a merry day once or twice in a man's life."

The only darkening element in his merriment is his habit of examining it too anxiously. So greedy is he of delight that he cannot let himself go, but must needs be measuring the extent to which he has achieved his desire. Sometimes he finds himself "merry," but at other times only "pretty merry." And there is one significant confession in connection with some performance of a favourite play, "and indeed it is good, though wronged by my over great expectations, as all things else are." This is one of the very few touches of anything approaching to cynicism which are to be found in his writings. His greed of merriment overleaps itself, and the confession of that is the deepest note in all his music.

Thus all the avenues leading beyond the earth were blocked. Other men escape along the lines of kindliness, love of friends, art, poetry, or religion. In all these avenues he walks or dances, but they lead him nowhere. At the bars he stands, an absolute worldling and pagan, full of an insatiable curiosity and an endless hunger and thirst. There is no touch of eternity upon his soul: his universe is Vanity Fair.

LECTURE VII

SARTOR RESARTUS

WE now begin the study of the last of the three stages in the battle between paganism and idealism. Having seen something of its primitive and classical forms, we took a cross section of it in the seventeenth century, and now we shall review one or two of its phases in our own time. The leap from the seventeenth century to the twentieth necessarily omits much that is vital and interesting. The eighteenth century, in its stately and complacent fashion, produced some of the most deliberate and finished types of paganism which the world has seen, and these were opposed by memorable antagonists. We cannot linger there, however, but must pass on to that great book which sounded the loudest bugle-note which the nineteenth century heard calling men to arms in this warfare.

Nothing could be more violent than the sudden transition from Samuel Pepys, that inveterate tumbler in the masque of life, whose absurdities and antics we have been looking at but now, to this solemn and tremendous book. Great in its own right, it is still greater when we remember that it stands at the beginning of the modern conflict between the material and spiritual development of England. Every student of the fourteenth century is familiar with two great figures, typical of the two contrasted features of its life. On the one hand stands Chaucer, with his infinite human interest, his good-humour, and his inexhaustible delight in man's life upon the earth. On the other hand, dark in shadows as Chaucer is bright with sunshine, stands Langland, colossal in his sadness, perplexed as he faces the facts of public life which are still our problems, earnest as death. There is no one figure which corresponds to Chaucer in the modern age, but Carlyle is certainly the counterpart of Langland. Standing in the shadow, he sends forth his great voice to his times, now breaking into sobs of pity, and anon into shrieks of hoarse laughter, terrible to hear. He, too, is bewildered, and he comes among his fellows "determined to pluck out the heart of the mystery"—the mystery alike of his own times and of general human life and destiny.

The book is in a great measure autobiographical, and is drawn from deep wells of experience, thought, and feeling. Inasmuch as its writer was a very typical Scotsman, it also was in a sense a manifesto of the national convictions which had made much of the noblest part of Scottish history, and which have served to stiffen the new races with which Scottish emigrants have blended, and to put iron into their blood. It is a book of incalculable importance, and if it be the case that it finds fewer readers in the rising generation than it did among their fathers, it is time that we returned to it. It is for want of such strong meat as this that the spirit of an age tends to grow feeble.

The object of the present lecture is neither to explain *Sartor Resartus* nor to summarise it. It certainly requires explanation, and it is no wonder that it puzzled the publishers. Before it was finally accepted by Fraser, its author had "carried it about for some two years from one terrified owl to another." When it appeared, the criticisms passed on it were amusing enough. Among those mentioned by Professor Nichol are, "A heap of clotted nonsense," and "When is that stupid series of articles by the crazy tailor going to end?" A book which could call forth such abuse, even from the dullest of minds, is certainly in need of elucidation. Yet here, more perhaps than in any other volume one could name, the interpretation must come from within. The truth which it has to declare will appeal to each reader in the light of his own experience of life. And the endeavour of the present lecture will simply be to give a clue to its main purpose. Every reader, following up that clue for himself, may find the growing interest and the irresistible fascination which the Victorians found in it. And when we add that without some knowledge of *Sartor* it is impossible to understand any serious book that has been written since it appeared, we do not exaggerate so much as might be supposed on the first hearing of so extraordinary a statement.

The first and chief difficulty with most readers is a very obvious and elementary one. What is it all about? As you read, you can entertain no doubt about the eloquence, the violent and unrestrained earnestness of purpose, the unmistakable reserves of power behind the detonating words and unforgettable phrases. But, after all, what is it that the man is trying to say? This is certainly an unpromising beginning. Other great prophets have prophesied in the vernacular; but "he that speaketh in an unknown tongue speaketh not unto men but unto God; for no man understandeth him; howbeit in the spirit he speaketh mysteries." Yet there are some things which cannot convey their full meaning in the vernacular, thoughts which must coin a language for themselves; and although at first there may be much bewilderment and even irritation, yet in the end we shall confess that the prophecy has found its proper language.

Let us go back to the time in which the book was written. In the late twenties and early thirties of the nineteenth century a quite exceptional group of men and women were writing books. It was one of those galaxies that now and then over-crowd the literary heavens with stars. To mention only a few of the famous names, there were Byron, Scott, Wordsworth, Dickens, Tennyson, and the Brownings. It fills one with envy to think of days when any morning might bring a new volume from any one of these. Emerson was very much alive then, and was already corresponding with Carlyle. Goethe died in 1832, but not before he had found in Carlyle one who "is almost more at home in our literature than ourselves," and who had penetrated to the innermost core of the German writings of his day.

At that time, too, momentous changes were coming upon the industrial and political life of England. In 1830 the Liverpool and Manchester Railway was opened, and in 1832 the Reform Bill was passed. Men were standing in the backwash of the French Revolution. The shouts of acclamation with which the promise of that dawn was hailed, had been silenced long ago by the bloody spectacle of Paris and the career of Napoleon Buonaparte. The day of Byronism was over, and polite England was already settling down to the conventionalities of the Early Victorian period. The romantic school was passing away, and the new generation was turning from it to seek reality in physical science. But deep below the conventionality and the utilitarianism alike there remained from the Revolution its legacy of lawlessness, and many were more intent on adventure than on obedience.

It was in the midst of this confused *mêlée* of opinions and impulses that Thomas Carlyle strode into the lists with his strange book. On the one hand it is a Titanic defence of the universe against the stage Titanism of Byron's *Cain*. On the other hand it is a revolt of reality against the empire of proprieties and appearances and shams. In a generation divided between the red cap of France and the coal-scuttle bonnet of England Carlyle stands bareheaded under the stars. Along with him stand Benjamin Disraeli, combining a genuine sympathy for the poor with a most grotesque delight in the aristocracy; and John Henry Newman, fierce against the Liberals, and yet the author of "Lead, kindly Light."

The book was handicapped more heavily by its own style than perhaps any book that ever fought its way from neglect and vituperation to idolatrous popularity. There is in it an immense amount of gag and patter, much of which is brilliant, but so wayward and fantastic as to give a sense of restlessness and perpetual noise. The very title is provoking, and not less so is the explanation of it—the pretended discovery of a German volume upon "Clothes, their origin and influence," published by Stillschweigen and Co., of Weissnichtwo, and written by Diogenes Teufelsdröckh. The puffs from the local newspaper, and the correspondence with Hofrath "Grasshopper," in no wise lessen the odds against such a work being taken seriously.

Again, as might be expected of a Professor of "Things in General," the book is discursive to the point of bewilderment. The whole progeny of "aerial, aquatic, and terrestrial devils" breaks loose upon us just as we are about to begin such a list of human apparel as never yet was published save in the catalogue of a museum collected by a madman. A dog with a tin kettle at his tail rushes mad and jingling across the street, leaving behind him a new view of the wild tyranny of Ambition. A great personage loses much sawdust through a rent in his unfortunate nether garments. Sirius and the Pleiades look down from above. The book is everywhere, and everywhere at once. The *asides* seem to occupy more space than the main thesis, whatever that may be. Just when you think you have found the meaning of the author at last, another display of these fireworks distracts your attention. It is not dark enough to see their full splendour, yet they confuse such daylight as you have.

Yet the main thesis cannot long remain in doubt. Through whatever amazement and distraction, it becomes clear enough at last. Clothes, which at once reveal and hide the man who wears them, are an allegory of the infinitely varied aspects and appearances of the world, beneath which lurk ultimate realities. But essential man is a naked animal, not a clothed one, and truth can only be arrived at by the most drastic stripping off of unreal appearances that cover it. The Professor will not linger upon the consideration of the lord's star or the clown's button, which are all that most men care to see: he will get down to the essential lord and the essential clown. And this will be more than an interesting literary occupation to him, or it will not long be that. Truth and God are one, and the devil is the prince of lies. This philosophy of clothes, then, is religion and not *belles lettres*. The reason for our sojourn on earth, and the only ground of any hope for a further sojourn elsewhere, is that in God's name we do battle with the devil.

The quest of reality must obviously be wide as

the universe, but if we are to engage in it to any purpose we must definitely begin it *somewhere.* A treatise on reality may easily be the most unreal of things—a mere battle in the air. So long as it is a discussion of theories it has this danger, and the first necessity is to bring the search down to the region of experience and rigorously insist on its remaining there. For this end the device of biography is adopted, and we see the meaning of all that apparent byplay of the six paper bags, and of the Weissnichtwo allusions which drop as puzzling fragments into Book I. The second book is wholly biographical. It is in human life and experience that we must fight our way through delusive appearances to reality; and Carlyle constructs a typical and immortal biography.

To the childless old people, Andreas and Gretchen Futteral, leading their sweet orchard life, there comes, in the dusk of evening, a stranger of reverend aspect—comes, and leaves with them the "invaluable Loan" of the baby Teufelsdröckh. Thenceforward, beside the little Kuhbach stream, we watch the opening out of a human life, from infancy to boyhood, and from boyhood to manhood. The story has been told a million times, but never quite in this fashion before. For rough delicacy, for exquisitely tender sternness, the biography is unique.

From the sleep of mere infancy the child is

awakened to the consciousness of creatorship by the gift of tools with which to make things. Tales open up for him the long vistas of history; and the stage-coach with its slow rolling blaze of lights teaches him geography, and the far-flung imaginative suggestiveness of the road; while the annual cattle-fair actually gathers the ends of the earth about his wondering eyes, and gives him his first impression of the variety of human life.

Childhood brings with it much that is sweet and gentle, flowing on like the little Kuhbach; and yet suggests far thoughts of Time and Eternity, concerning which we are evidently to hear more before the end. The formal education he receives —that "wood and leather education"—calls forth only protest. But the development of his spirit proceeds in spite of it. So far as the passive side of character goes, he does excellently. On the active side things go not so well. Already he begins to chafe at the restraints of obedience, and the youthful spirit is beating against its bars. The stupidities of an education which only appeals to the one faculty of memory, and to that mainly by means of birch-rods, increase the rebellion, and the sense of restraint is brought to a climax when at last old Andreas dies. Then "the dark bottomless Abyss, that lies under our feet, had yawned open; the pale kingdoms of Death, with all their innumerable silent nations and generations, stood before him ; the inexorable word NEVER ! now first showed its meaning."

The youth is now ready to enter, as such a one inevitably must, upon the long and losing battle of faith and doubt. He is at the theorising stage as yet, not having learned to make anything, but only to discuss things. And yet the time is not wasted if the mind have been taught to think. For "truly a Thinking Man is the worst enemy the Prince of Darkness can have."

The immediate consequence and employment of this unripe time of half-awakened manhood is, however, unsatisfactory enough. There is much reminiscence of early Edinburgh days, with their law studies, and tutoring, and translating, in Teufelsdröckh's desultory period. The climax of it is in those scornful sentences about Aesthetic Teas, to which the hungry lion was invited, that he might feed on chickweed—well for all concerned if it did not end in his feeding on the chickens instead! It is an unwholesome time with the lad—a time of sullen contempt alternating with loud rebellion, of mingled vanity and self-indulgence, and of much sheer devilishness of temper.

Upon this exaggerated and most disagreeable period, lit by "red streaks of unspeakable grandeur, yet also in the blackness of darkness," there comes suddenly the master passion of romantic love. Had this adventure proved successful, we should have simply had the old story, which ends in "so they lived happily ever after." What the net result of all the former strivings after truth and freedom would have been, we need not inquire. For this is another story, equally old and to the end of time ever newly repeated. There is much of Werther in it, and still more of Jean Paul Richter. Its finest English counterpart is Longfellow's *Hyperion*—the most beautiful piece of our literature, surely, that has ever been forgotten—in which Richter's story lives again. But never has the tale been more exquisitely told than in *Sartor Resartus*. For one sweet hour of life the youth has been taken out of himself and pale doubt flees far away. Life, that has been but a blasted heath, blooms suddenly with unheard-of blossoms of hope and of delight. Then comes the end. "Their lips were joined, their two souls, like two dewdrops, rushed into one,—for the first time, and for the last! Thus was Teufelsdröckh made immortal by a Kiss. And then? Why, then—thick curtains of Night rushed over his soul, as rose the immeasurable Crash of Doom; and through the ruins as of a shivered Universe was he falling, falling, towards the Abyss."

The sorrows of Teufelsdröckh are but too well

known. Flung back upon his former dishevelment of mind from so great and calm a height, the crash must necessarily be terrible. Yet he will not take up his life where he left it to follow Blumine. Such an hour inevitably changes a man, for better or for worse. There is at least a dignity about him now, even while the "nameless Unrest" urges him forward through his darkened world. The scenes of his childhood in the little Entepfuhl bring no consolation. Nature, even in his wanderings among her mountains, is equally futile, for the wanderer can never escape from his own shadow among her solitudes. Yet is his nature not dissolved, but only "compressed closer," as it were, and we watch the next stage of this development with a sense that some mysteriously great and splendid experience is on the eve of being born.

Thus we come to those three central chapters—chapters so fundamental and so true to human life, that it is safe to prophesy that they will be familiar so long as books are read upon the earth—"The Everlasting No," "Centre of Indifference" and "The Everlasting Yea."

In "The Everlasting No" we watch the work of negation upon the soul of man. His life has capitulated to the Spirit that denies, and the unbelief is as bitter as it is hopeless. "Doubt had darkened into Unbelief; shade after shade goes grimly over your soul, till you have the fixed, starless, Tartarean black." "Is there no God, then; but at best an absentee God, sitting idle, ever since the first Sabbath, at the outside of his Universe, and *seeing* it go? Has the word Duty no meaning?"

"Thus has the bewildered Wanderer to stand, as so many have done, shouting question after question into the Sibyl-cave of Destiny, and receive no Answer but an Echo." Faith, indeed, lies dormant but alive beneath the doubt. But in the meantime the man's own weakness paralyses action; and, while this paralysis lasts, all faith appears to have departed. He has ceased to believe in himself, and to believe in his friends. "The very Devil has been pulled down, you cannot so much as believe in a Devil. To me the Universe was all void of Life, of Purpose, of Volition, even of Hostility: it was one huge, dead, immeasurable Steam-engine, rolling on, in its dead indifference, to grind men limb from limb. O, the vast, gloomy, solitary Golgotha, and Mill of Death!"

He is saved from suicide simply by the aftershine of Christianity. The religion of his fathers lingers, no longer as a creed, but as a powerful set of associations and emotions. It is a small thing to cling to amid the wrack of a man's universe; yet it holds until the appearance of a new phase in which he is to find escape from the prison-house. He has begun to realise that fear—a nameless fear of he knows not what—has taken hold upon him. "I lived in a continual, indefinite, pining fear; tremulous, pusillanimous." Fear affects men in widely different ways. We have seen how this same vague "sense of enemies" obsessed the youthful spirit of Marius the Epicurean, until it cleared itself eventually into the conscience of a Christian man. But Teufelsdröckh is prouder and more violent of spirit than the sedate and patrician Roman, and he leaps at the throat of fear in a wild defiance. "What *art* thou afraid of? Wherefore, like a coward, dost thou forever pip and whimper, and go cowering and trembling? Despicable biped! What is the sum-total of the worst that lies before thee? Death? Well, Death: and say the pangs of Tophet too, and all that the Devil and Man may, will or can do against thee! Hast thou not a Heart; canst thou not suffer whatsoever it be; and, as a Child of Freedom, though outcast, trample Tophet itself under thy feet, while it consumes thee? Let it come, then; I will meet it and defy it!"

This is no permanent or stable resting-place, but it is the beginning of much. It is the assertion of self in indignation and wild defiance, instead of the former misery of a man merely haunted by himself. This is that "Baphometic Fire-baptism" or new-birth of spiritual awakening, which is the beginning of true manhood. The Everlasting No had said: "Behold, thou art fatherless, outcast, and the Universe is mine (the Devil's); to which my whole Me now made answer: I am not thine, but Free, and forever hate thee!"

The immediate result of this awakening is told in "Centre of Indifference"—*i.e.*, indifference to oneself, one's own feelings, and even to fate. It is the transition from subjective to objective interests, from eating one's own heart out to a sense of the wide and living world by which one is surrounded. It is the same process which, just about this time, Robert Browning was describing in *Paracelsus* and *Sordello.* Once more Teufelsdröckh travels, but this time how differently! Instead of being absorbed by the haunting shadow of himself, he sees the world full of vital interests—cities of men, tilled fields, books, battlefields. The great questions of the world—the true meanings alike of peace and war—claim his interest. The great men, whether Goethe or Napoleon, do their work before his astonished eyes. "Thus can the Professor, at least in lucid intervals, look away from his own sorrows, over the many-coloured world, and pertinently enough note what is passing there." He has reached—strangely enough through self-assertion—the centre of indifference to self, and of interest in other people and things. And the supreme lesson of it all is the value of *efficiency*. Napoleon "was a Divine Missionary, though unconscious of it; and preached, through the cannon's throat, that great doctrine, *La carrière ouverte aux talens* (the tools to him that can handle them)."

This bracing doctrine carries us at once into The Everlasting Yea. It is not enough that a man pass from the morbid and self-centred mood to an interest in the outward world that surrounds him. That might transform him simply into a curious but heartless dilettante, a mere tourist of the spirit, whose sole desire is to see and to take notes. But that could never satisfy Carlyle; for that is but self-indulgence in its more refined form of the lust of the eyes. It was not for this that the Everlasting No had set Teufelsdröckh wailing, nor for this that he had risen up in wrath and bidden defiance to fear. From his temptation in the wilderness the Son of Man must come forth, not to wander open-mouthed about the plain, but to work his way "into the higher sunlit slopes of that Mountain which has no summit, or whose summit is in Heaven only."

In other words, a great compassion for his

fellow-men has come upon him. "With other eyes, too, could I now look upon my fellow-man: with an infinite Love, an infinite Pity. Poor, wandering, wayward man! Art thou not tried, and beaten with stripes, even as I am? Ever, whether thou bear the royal mantle or the beggar's gabardine, art thou not so weary, so heavy-laden; and thy Bed of Rest is but a Grave. O my Brother, my Brother, why cannot I shelter thee in my bosom, and wipe away all tears from thy eyes!" The words remind us of the famous passage, occurring early in the book, which describes the Professor's Watchtower. It was suggested by the close-packed streets of Edinburgh's poorer quarter, as seen from the slopes of the hills which stand close on her eastern side. Probably no passage ever written has so vividly and suggestively massed together the various and contradictory aspects of the human tragedy.

One more question, however, has yet to be answered before we have solved our problem. What about happiness? We all cry aloud for it, and make its presence or absence the criterion for judging the worth of days. Teufelsdröckh goes to the heart of the matter with his usual directness. It is this search for happiness which is the explanation of all the unwholesomeness that culminated in the Everlasting No. "Because the THOU (sweet gentleman) is not sufficiently honoured, nourished, soft-bedded, and lovingly cared-for? Foolish soul! What Act of Legislature was there that *thou* shouldst be Happy? A little while ago thou hadst no right to *be* at all. What if thou wert born and predestined not to be Happy, but to be Unhappy! Art thou nothing other than a Vulture, then, that fliest through the Universe seeking after somewhat to *eat*; and shrieking dolefully because carrion enough is not given thee? Close thy *Byron*; open thy *Goethe*." In effect, happiness is a relative term, which we can alter as we please by altering the amount which we demand from life. "Fancy that thou deservest to be hanged (as is most likely), thou wilt feel it happiness to be only shot: fancy that thou deservest to be hanged in a hair-halter, it will be a luxury to die in hemp."

Such teaching is neither sympathetic enough nor positive enough to be of much use to poor mortals wrestling with their deepest problems. Yet in the very negation of happiness he discovers a positive religion—the religion of the Cross, the Worship of Sorrow. Expressed crudely, this seems to endorse the ascetic fallacy of the value of self-denial for its own sake. But from that it is saved by the divine element in sorrow which Christ has brought—"Love not Pleasure; love God. This is the EVERLASTING YEA, wherein all contradiction is solved : wherein whoso walks and works, it is well with him."

This still leaves us perilously near to morbidness. The Worship of Sorrow might well be but a natural and not less morbid reaction from the former morbidness, the worship of self and happiness. From that, however, it is saved by the word "works," which is spoken with emphasis in this connection. So we pass to the last phase of the Everlasting Yea, in which we return to the thesis upon which we began, viz., that "Doubt of any sort cannot be removed except by action." "Do the Duty which *lies nearest thee,* which thou knowest to be a Duty! Thy second Duty will already have become clearer. . . . Yes here, in this poor, miserable, hampered, despicable Actual, wherein thou even now standest, here or nowhere is thy Ideal; work it out therefrom; and working, believe, live, be free. . . . Produce! Produce! Were it but the pitifullest infinitesimal fraction of a Product, produce it, in God's name! 'Tis the utmost thou hast in thee; out with it, then. Up, up! Whatsoever thy hand findeth to do, do it with thy whole might. Work while it is called Today; for the Night cometh, wherein no man can work."

Thus the goal of human destiny is not any theory, however true; not any happiness, however alluring. It is for practical purposes that the universe is built, and he who would be "in tune with the universe" must first and last be practical. In various forms this doctrine has reappeared and shown itself potent. Ritschl based his system on practical values in religion, and Professor William James has proclaimed the same doctrine in a still wider application in his Pragmatism. The essential element in both systems is that they lay the direct stress of life, not upon abstract theory but upon experience and vital energy. This transference from theorising and emotionalism to the prompt and vigorous exercise of will upon the immediate circumstance, is Carlyle's understanding of the word Conversion.

When it comes to the particular question of what work the Professor is to do, the answer is that he has within him the Word Omnipotent, waiting for a man to speak it forth. And here in this volume upon Clothes, this *Sartor Resartus*, is his deliberate response to the great demand. At first he seems here to relapse from the high seriousness of the chapters we have just been reading, and to come with too great suddenness to earth again. Yet that is not the case; for, as we shall see, the rest of the volume is the attempt to reconstruct the universe on the principles he has discovered within his own experience. The story to which we have been listening is Teufelsdröckh's way of discovering reality; now we are to have the statement of it on the wider planes of social and other philosophy. This we shall briefly review, but the gist of the book is in what we have already found. To most readers the quotations must have been old and well-remembered friends. Yet they will pardon the reappearance of them here, for they have been amongst the most powerful of all wingéd words spoken in England for centuries. The reason for the popularity of the book is that these biographical chapters are the record of normal and typical human experience. This, or something like this, will repeat itself so long as human nature lasts; and men, grown discouraged with the mystery and bewilderment of life, will find heart from these chapters to start "once more on their adventure, brave and new."

This, then, is Teufelsdröckh's reconstruction of the world; and the world of each one of us requires some such reconstruction. For life is full of deceptive outward appearances, from which it is the task of every man to come back in his own way to the realities within. The shining example of such reconstruction is that of George Fox, who sewed himself a suit of leather and went out to the woods with it—"Every stitch of his needle pricking into the heart of slavery, and world-worship, and the Mammon god." The leather suit is an allegory of the whole. The appearances of men and things are but the fantastic clothes with which they cover their nakedness. They take these clothes of theirs to be themselves, and the first duty and only hope of a man is to divest himself of all such coverings, and discover what manner of man he really is.

This process of divesting, however, may yield either of two results. A man may take, for the reality of himself, either the low view of human nature, in which man is but "a forked straddling animal with bandy legs," or the high view, in which he is a spirit, and unutterable Mystery of Mysteries. It is the latter view which Thomas Carlyle champions, through this and many other volumes, against the materialistic thought of his time.

The chapter on Dandies is a most extraordinary attack on the keeping up of appearances. The Dandy is he who not only keeps up appearances but actually worships them. He is their advocate and special pleader. His very office and function is to wear clothes. Here we have the illusion stripped from much that we have taken for reality. Sectarianism is a prominent example of it, the reading of fashionable novels is another. In the former two are seen the robes of eternity flung over one very vulgar form of self-worship, and in the latter the robe of fashionable society is flung over another. The reality of man's intercourse with Eternity and with his fellow-men has died within these vestures, but the eyes of the public are satisfied, and never guess the corpse within. Sectarianism and Vanity Fair are but common forms of self-worship, in which every one is keeping up appearances, and is so intent upon that exercise that all thought of reality has vanished.

A shallower philosopher would have been content with exposing these and other shams; and consequently his philosophy would have led nowhere. Carlyle is a greater thinker, and one who takes a wider view. He is no enemy of clothes, although fools have put them to wrong uses and made them the instruments of deception. His choice is not between worshipping and abandoning the world and its appearances. He will frankly confess the value of it and of its vesture, and so we have the chapter on Adamitism, in defence of clothes, which acknowledges in great and ingenious detail the many uses of the existing order of institutions. But still, through all such acknowledgment, we are reminded constantly of the main truth. All appearance is for the sake of reality, and all tools for expressing the worker. When the appearance becomes a substitute for the reality, and the tools absorb the attention that should be devoted to the work for whose accomplishment they exist, then we have relapsed into the fundamental human error. The object of the book is to plunge back from appearance to reality, from clothes to him who wears them. "Who am I? What is this ME? . . . some embodied, visualised Idea in the Eternal Mind."

This swift retreat upon reality occurs at intervals throughout the whole book, and in connection with every conceivable department of human life and interest. In many parts there is little attempt at sequence or order. The author has made voluminous notes on men and things, and the whole fantastic structure of *Sartor Resartus* is a device for introducing these disjointedly. In the remainder of this lecture we shall select and displace freely, in order to present the main teachings of the book in manageable groups.

1. *Language and Thought.*—Language is the natural garment of thoughts, and while sometimes it performs its function of revealing them, it often conceals them. Many people's whole intellectual life is spent in dealing with words, and they never penetrate to the thoughts at all. Still more commonly, people get lost among words, especially words which have come to be used metaphorically, and again fail to penetrate to the thought. Thus the *Name* is the first garment wrapped around the

essential ME; and all speech, whether of science, poetry, or politics, is simply an attempt at right naming. The names by which we call things are apt to become labelled pigeon-holes in which we bury them. Having catalogued and indexed our facts, we lose sight of them thenceforward, and think and speak in terms of the catalogue. If you are a Liberal, it is possible that all you may know or care to know about Conservatism is the name. Nay, having catalogued yourself a Liberal, you may seldom even find it necessary to inquire what the significance of Liberalism really is. If you happen to be a Conservative, the corresponding risks will certainly not be less.

The dangers of these word-garments, and the habit of losing all contact with reality in our constant habit of living among mere words, naturally suggest to Carlyle his favourite theme—a plea for silence. We all talk too much, and the first lesson we have to learn on our way to reality is to be oftener silent. This duty of silence, as has been wittily remarked, Carlyle preaches in thirty-seven volumes of eloquent English speech. "SILENCE and SECRECY! Altars might still be raised to them (were this an altar-building time) for universal worship. Silence is the element in which great things fashion themselves together; that at length they may emerge, full-formed and majestic, into the daylight of Life, which they are thenceforth to rule. . . . Nay, in thy own mean perplexities, do thou thyself but *hold thy tongue for one day*: on the morrow how much clearer are thy purposes and duties." Andreas, in his old camp-sentinel days, once challenged the emperor himself with the demand for the password. "Schweig, Hund!" replied Frederich; and Andreas, telling the tale in after years would add, "There is what I call a King."

Yet silence may be as devoid of reality as words, and most minds require something external to quicken thought and fill up the emptiness of their silences. So we have symbols, whose doctrine is here most eloquently expounded. Man is not ruled by logic but by imagination, and a thousand thoughts will rise at the call of some well-chosen symbol. In itself it may be the poorest of things, with no intrinsic value at all—a clouted shoe, an iron crown, a flag whose market value may be almost nothing. Yet such a thing may so work upon men's silences as to fill them with the glimmer of a divine idea.

Other symbols there are which *have* intrinsic value—works of art, lives of heroes, death itself, in all of which we may see Eternity working through Time, and become aware of Reality amid the passing shows. Religious symbols are the highest of all, and highest among these stands Jesus of Nazareth. "Higher has the human Thought not yet reached: this is Christianity and Christendom; a symbol of quite perennial, infinite character; whose significance will ever demand to be anew enquired into, and anew made manifest." In other words, Jesus stands for all that is permanently noble and permanently real in human life.

Such symbols as have intrinsic value are indeed perennial. Time at length effaces the others; they lose their associations, and become but meaningless lumber. But these significant works and personalities can never grow effete. They tell their own story to the succeeding generations, blessing them with visions of reality and preserving them from the Babel of meaningless words.

2. *Body and Spirit.*—Souls are "rendered visible in bodies that took shape and will lose it, melting into air." Thus bodies, and not spirits, are the true apparitions, the souls being the realities which they both reveal and hide. In fact, body is literally a garment of flesh—a garment which the soul has for a time put on, but which it will lay aside again. One of the greatest of all the idolatries of appearance is our constant habit of judging one another by the attractiveness of the bodily vesture. Many of the judgments which we pass upon our fellows would be reversed if we trained ourselves to look

through the vestures of flesh to the men themselves—the souls that are hidden within.

The natural expansion of this is in the general doctrine of matter and spirit. Purely material science—science which has lost the faculty of wonder and of spiritual perception—is no true science at all. It is but a pair of spectacles without an eye. For all material things are but emblems of spiritual things—shadows or images of things in the heavens—and apart from these they have no reality at all.

3. *Society and Social Problems.*—It follows naturally that a change must come upon our ways of regarding the relations of man to man. If every man is indeed a temple of the divine, and therefore to be revered, then much of our accepted estimates and standards of social judgment will have to be abandoned. Society, as it exists, is founded on class distinctions which largely consist in the exaltation of idleness and wealth. Against this we have much eloquent protest. "Venerable to me is the hard hand; crooked, coarse; wherein notwithstanding lies a cunning virtue, indefeasibly royal, as of the Sceptre of this Planet. Venerable too is the rugged face, all weather-tanned, besoiled, with its rude intelligence; for it is the face of a Man living man like." How far away we are from all this with

our mammon-worship and our fantastic social unrealities, every student of our times must know, or at least must have often heard. He would not have heard it so often, however, had not Thomas Carlyle cried it out with that harsh voice of his, in this and many others of his books. It was his gunpowder, more than any other explosive of the nineteenth century, that broke up the immense complacency into which half England always tends to relapse.

He is not hopeless of the future of society. Society is the true Phœnix, ever repeating the miracle of its resurrection from the ashes of the former fire. There are indestructible elements in the race of man—"organic filaments" he calls them — which bind society together, and which ensure a future for the race after any past, however lamentable. Those "organic filaments" are Carlyle's idea of Social Reality—the real things which survive all revolution. There are four such realities which ensure the future for society even when it seems extinct.

First, there is the fact of man's brotherhood to man—a fact quite independent of man's willingness to acknowledge that brotherhood. Second, there is the common bond of tradition, and all our debt to the past, which is a fact equally independent of our willingness to acknowledge it. Third, there is the natural and inevitable fact of man's necessity for reverencing some one above him. Obedience and reverence are forthcoming, whenever man is in the presence of what he *ought* to reverence, and so hero-worship is secure.

These three bonds of social reality are inseparable from one another. The first, the brotherhood of man, has often been used as the watchword of a false independence. It is only possible on the condition of reverence and obedience for that which is higher than oneself, either in the past or the present. "Suspicion of 'Servility,' of reverence for Superiors, the very dog-leech is anxious to disavow. Fools! Were your Superiors worthy to govern, and you worthy to obey, reverence for them were even your only possible freedom." These three, then, are the social realities, and all other social distinctions and conventionalities are but clothes, to be replaced or thrown away at need.

But there is a fourth bond of social reality—the greatest and most powerful of all. That reality is Religion. Here, too, we must distinguish clothes from that which they cover—forms of religion from religion itself. Church-clothes, indeed, are as necessary as any other clothes, and they will harm no one who remembers that they are but clothes, and distinguishes between faith and form. The old forms are already being discarded, yet Religion is so vital that it will always find new forms for itself, suited to the new age. For religion, in one form or in another, is absolutely essential to society; and, being a grand reality, will continue to keep society from collapse.

4. From this we pass naturally to the great and final doctrine in which the philosophy of clothes is expounded. That doctrine, condensed into a single sentence, is that "the whole Universe is the Garment of God." This brings us back to the song of the *Erdgeist* in Goethe's *Faust*:—

> "In Being's floods, in Action's storm,
> I walk and work, above, beneath,
> Work and weave in endless motion!
> Birth and Death,
> An infinite ocean;
> A seizing and giving
> The fire of Living:
> 'Tis thus at the roaring Loom of Time I ply,
> And weave for God the Garment thou seest Him by."

This is, of course, no novelty invented by Goethe. We find it in Marius the Epicurean, and he found it in ancient wells of Greek philosophy. Carlyle's use of it has often been taken for Pantheism. In so mystic a region it is impossible to expect precise theological definition, and yet it is right to remember that Carlyle does not identify the garment with its Wearer. The whole argument of the book is to distinguish appearance from reality in every instance, and this is no exception. "What is Nature? Ha! why do I not name thee God? Art thou not the 'living garment of God'? O Heavens, is it in very deed He, then, that ever speaks through thee? that lives and loves in thee, that lives and loves in me? . . . The Universe is not dead and demoniacal, a charnel-house with spectres: but godlike and my Father's." "This fair Universe, were it in the meanest province thereof, is in very deed the star-domed City of God; through every star, through every grass-blade, and most through every Living Soul, the glory of a present God still beams. But Nature, which is the Time-vesture of God, and reveals Him to the wise, hides Him from the foolish."

Such is some very broken sketch of this great book. It will at least serve to recall to the memory of some readers thoughts and words which long ago stirred their blood in youth. No volume could so fitly be chosen as a background against which to view the modern surge of the age-long battle. But the charm of *Sartor Resartus* is, after all, personal. We go back to the life-story of Teufelsdröckh, out of which such varied and such lofty teachings sprang, and we read it over and over again because we find in it so much that is our own story too.

LECTURE VIII

PAGAN REACTIONS

In the last lecture we began the study of the modern aspects of our subject with Carlyle's *Sartor Resartus*. Now, in a rapid sketch, we shall look at some of the writings which followed that great book; and, with it as background, we shall see them in stronger relief. It is impossible to overestimate the importance of the influence which was wielded by Carlyle, and especially by his *Sartor Resartus*. His was a gigantic power, both in literature and in morals. At first, as we have already noted, he met with neglect and ridicule in abundance, but afterwards these passed into sheer wonder, and then into a wide and devoted worship. Everybody felt his power, and all earnest thinkers were seized in the strong grip of reality with which he laid hold upon his time.

The religious thought and faith both of England and of Scotland felt him, but his mark was deepest upon Scotland, because of two interesting facts.

First of all, Carlyle represented that old Calvinism which had always fitted so exactly the national character and spirit; and second, there were in Scotland many people who, while retaining the Calvinistic spirit, had lost touch with the old definite creed. Nothing could be more characteristic of Carlyle than this Calvinism of the spirit which had passed beyond the letter of the old faith. He stands like an old Covenanter in the mist; and yet a Covenanter grasping his father's iron sword. It is because of these two facts *Sartor Resartus* has taken so prominent a place in our literature. It stands for a kind of conscience behind the manifold modern life of our day. Beneath the shrieks and the laughter of the time we hear in it the boom of great breakers. Never again can we forget, amidst the gaieties of any island paradise, the solemn ocean that surrounds it. Carlyle's teaching sounds and recurs again and again like the Pilgrims' March in *Tannhäuser* breaking through the overture, and rivalling until it vanquishes the music of the Venusberg.

Yet it was quite inevitable that there should be strong reaction from any such work as this. To the warm blood and the poignant sense of the beauty of the world it brought a sense of chill, a forbidding sombreness and austerity. Carlyle's conception of Christianity was that of the worship of sorrow; and, while the essence of his gospel was labour, yet to many minds self-denial seemed to be no longer presented, as in the teaching of Jesus, as a means towards the attainment of further spiritual ends. It had become an end in itself, and one that few would desire or feel to be justified. In the reaction it was felt that self-development had claims upon the human spirit as well as self-denial, and indeed that the happy instincts of life had no right to be so winsome unless they were meant to be obeyed. The beauty of the world could not be regarded as a mere trap for the tempting of people, if one were to retain any worthy conception of the Powers that govern the world. From this point of view the Carlylians appeared to enter into life maimed. That, indeed, we all must do, as Christ told us; but they seemed to do it like the beggars of Colombo, with a deliberate and somewhat indecent exhibition of their wounds.

Carlyle found many men around him pagan, worshipping the earth without any spiritual light in them. He feared that many others were about to go in the same direction, so he cried aloud that the earth was too small, and that they must find a larger object of worship. For the earth he substituted the universe, and led men's eyes out among the immensities and eternities. Professor James tells a story of Margaret Fuller, the American transcendentalist, having said with folded hands, "I accept the universe," and how Carlyle, hearing this, had answered, "Gad, she'd better!" It was this insistence upon the universe, as distinguished from the earth, which was the note of *Sartor Resartus.*

The reactionaries took Carlyle at his word. They said, "Yes, we shall worship the universe"; but they went on to add that Carlyle's universe is not universal. It is at once too vague and too austere. There are other elements in life besides those to which he called attention—elements very definite and not at all austere—and they too have a place in the universe and a claim upon our acceptance. Many of these are in every way more desirable to the type of mind that rebelled than the aspects of the universe on which Carlyle had insisted, and so they went out freely among these neglected elements, set them over against his kind of idealism, and became themselves idealists of other sorts.

Matthew Arnold, the apostle of culture, found his idealism in the purely mental region. Rossetti was the idealist of the heart, with its whole world of emotions, and that subtle and far-reaching interplay between soul and body for which Carlyle had always made too little allowance. Mr. H. G. Wells and Mr. Bernard Shaw, proclaiming themselves idealists of the social order, have been reaching conclusions and teaching doctrines at which Carlyle would have stood aghast. These are but random examples, but they are one in this, that each has protested against that one-sidedness for which Carlyle stood. Yet each is a one-sided protest, and falls again into the snare of setting the affections upon things which are not eternal, and so wedding man to the green earth again.

Thus we find paganism — in some quarters paganism quite openly confessed—occupying a prominent place in our literature to-day. Before we examine some of its aspects in detail a word or two of preliminary warning may be permissible. It is a mistake to take the extremer forms of this reaction too seriously, although at the present time this is very frequently done. One must remember that such a spirit as this is to be found in every age, and that it always creates an ephemeral literature which imagines itself to be a lasting one. It is nothing new. It is as old and as perennial as the complex play of the human mind and human society.

Another reason for not taking this phase too seriously is that it was quite inevitable that some such reaction should follow upon the huge solemnities of Carlyle. Just as in literature, after the classic formality of Johnson and his contemporaries, there must come the reaction of the Romantic School, which includes Sir Walter Scott, Byron, and Burns; so here there must be an inevitable reaction from austerity to a daring freedom which will take many various forms. From Carlyle's solemnising liturgy we were bound to pass to the slang and colloquialism of the man in the street and the woman in the modern novel. Body and spirit are always in unstable equilibrium, and an excess of either at once swings the fashion back to the other extreme. Carlyle had his day largely in consequence of what one may call the eighteenth-century glut—the Georgian society and its economics, and the Byronic element in literature. The later swing back was as inevitable as Carlyle had been. Perhaps it was most clearly noticed after the deaths of Browning and Tennyson, in the late eighties and the early nineties. But both before and since that time it has been very manifest in England.

But beyond all these things there is the general fact that before any literature becomes pagan the land must first have been paganised. Of course there is always here again a reaction of mutual cause and effect between literature and national spirit. Carlyle himself, in his doctrine of heroes, was continually telling us that it is the personality which produces the *zeitgeist*, and not *vice versa*. On the other hand it is equally certain that no personality is independent of his age and the backing he finds in it, or the response which he may enlist for his revolt from it. Both of these are true statements of the case; as to which is ultimate, that is the old and rather academic question of whether the oak or the acorn comes first. We repeat that it is impossible, in this double play of cause and effect, to say which is the ultimate cause and which the effect. The controversy which was waged in the nineteenth century between the schools of Buckle and Carlyle is likely to go on indefinitely through the future. But what concerns us at present is this, that all paganism which finds expression in a literature has existed in the age before it found that expression. The literature is indeed to some extent the creator of the age, but to a far greater extent it is the expression of the age, whose creation is due to a vast multiplicity of causes.

Among these causes one of the foremost was political advance and freedom—the political doctrines, and the beginnings of Socialistic thought, which had appeared about the time when *Sartor Resartus* was written. The Reform Bill of 1832 tended to concentrate men's attention upon questions of material welfare. Commercial and industrial prosperity followed, keeping the nation busy with the earth. In very striking language Lord Morley describes this fact, in language specially striking as coming from so eminently progressive a man.[1] "Far the most penetrating of all the influences that are impairing the moral and intellectual nerve of our generation, remain still to be mentioned. The first of them is the immense increase of material prosperity, and the second is the immense decline in sincerity of spiritual interest. The evil wrought by the one fills up the measure of the evil wrought by the other. We have been, in spite of momentary declensions, on a flood-tide of high profits and a roaring trade, and there is nothing like a roaring trade for engendering latitudinarians. The effect of many possessions, especially if they be newly acquired, in slackening moral vigour, is a proverb. Our new wealth is hardly leavened by any tradition of public duty such as lingers among the English nobles, nor as yet by any common custom of devotion to public causes, such as seems to live and grow in the United States. Under such conditions, with new wealth come luxury and love of ease and that fatal readiness to believe that God has placed us in the best of possible worlds, which so lowers men's aims and unstrings

[1] *On Compromise*, published 1874.

their firmness of purpose. Pleasure saps high interests, and the weakening of high interests leaves more undisputed room for pleasure." "The political spirit has grown to be the strongest element in our national life; the dominant force, extending its influence over all our ways of thinking in matters that have least to do with politics, or even nothing at all to do with them. There has thus been engendered among us the real sense of political responsibility. In a corresponding degree has been discouraged . . . the sense of intellectual responsibility. . . . Practically, and as a matter of history, a society is seldom at the same time successfully energetic both in temporals and spirituals; seldom prosperous alike in seeking abstract truth and nursing the political spirit."

The result of the new phase of English life was, on the one hand, industrialism with its material values, and on the other hand the beginnings of a Socialism equally pagan. The motto of both schools was that a man's life consisteth in the abundance of the things that he possesseth, that you should seek first all these things, and that the Kingdom of God and His righteousness may be added unto you, if you have any room for them. Make yourself secure of all these other things; seek comfort whether you be rich or poor; make this world as agreeable to yourself as your means will allow, and seek to increase your means of making it still more agreeable. After you have done all that, anything that is left over will do for your idealism. Your God can be seen to after you have abundantly provided for the needs of your body. Nothing could be more characteristic paganism than this, which makes material comfort the real end of life, and all spiritual things a residual element. It is the story which Isaiah tells, with such sublimity of sarcasm, of the huntsman and craftsman who warms his hands and cries to himself, "Aha! I am warm. I have seen the fire." He bakes bread and roasts flesh, and, with the residue of the same log which he has used for kindling his fire, he maketh a god. So this modern god of England, when England had become materialised, was just that ancient fire-worship and comfort-worship in its nineteenth-century phase. In the first demand of life there is no thought of God or of idealism of any kind. These, if they appear at all, have to be made out of what is left. "Of the residue he maketh a god."

It is by insidious degrees that materialism invades a nation's life. At first it attacks the externals, appearing mainly in the region of work, wealth, and comfort. But, unless some check is put upon its progress, it steadily works its way to the central depths, attacking love and sorrow, and changing them to sensuality and cynicism. Then the nation's day is over, and its men and women are lost souls. Many instances might be quoted in which this progress has actually been made in the literature of England. At present we are only pointing to the undoubted fact that the forces of materialism have been at work among us. If proof of this were needed, nothing could afford it more clearly than our loss of peace and dignity in modern society. Many costly luxuries have become necessities, and they have increased the pace of life to a rush and fury which makes business a turmoil and social life a fever. A symbolic embodiment of this spirit may be seen in the motor car and the aeroplane as they are often used. These indeed need not be ministers of paganism. The glory of swift motion and the mounting up on wings as eagles reach very near to the spiritual, if not indeed across its borderland, as exhilarating and splendid stimuli to the human spirit. But, on the other hand, they may be merely instruments for gratifying that insane human restlessness which is but the craving for new sensations. Along the whole line of our commercial and industrial prosperity there runs one great division. There are some who, in the midst of all change, have preserved their old spiritual loyalties, and there are others who have substituted novelty for loyalty. These are the idealists and the pagans of the twentieth century.

Another potent factor in the making of the new times was the scientific advance which has made so remarkable a difference to the whole outlook of man upon the earth. Darwin's great discovery is perhaps the most epoch-making fact in science that has yet appeared upon the earth. The first apparent trend of evolution seemed to be an entirely materialistic reaction. This was due to the fact that believers in the spiritual had identified with their spirituality a great deal that was unnecessary and merely casual. If the balloon on which people mount up above the earth is any such theory as that of the six days' creation, it is easy to see how when that balloon is pricked the spiritual flight of the time appears to have ended on the ground.

Of course all that has long passed by. Of late years Haeckel has been crying out that all his old friends have deserted him and have gone over to the spiritual side—a cry which reminds one of the familiar juryman who finds his fellows the eleven most obstinate men he has ever known. The conception of evolution has long since been taken over by the idealists, and has become perhaps the most splendidly Christian and idealistic idea of the new age. When Darwin published his *Origin of Species*, Hegel cried out in Germany, "Darwin has destroyed design." To-day Darwin and Hegel stand together as the prophets of the unconquerable conviction of the reality of spirit. From the days of Huxley and Haeckel we have passed over to the days of Bergson and Sir Oliver Lodge.

The effect of all this upon individuals is a very interesting phenomenon to watch. Every one of us has been touched by the pagan spirit which has invaded our times at so many different points of entrance. It has become an atmosphere which we have all breathed more or less. If some one were to say to any company of British people, one by one, that they were pagans, doubtless many of them would resent it, and yet more or less it would true. We all are pagans; we cannot help ourselves, for every one of us is necessarily affected by the spirit of his generation. Nobody indeed says, "Go to, I will be a pagan"; but the old story of Aaron's golden calf repeats itself continually. Aaron, when Moses rebuked him, said naïvely, "There came out this calf." That exactly describes the situation. That calf is the only really authentic example of spontaneous generation, of effect without cause. Nobody expected it. Nobody wanted it. Everybody was surprised to see it when it came. It was the Melchizedek among cattle

—without father, without mother, without descent. Unfortunately it seems also to have been without beginning of days or end of life. Every generation simply puts in its gold and there comes out this calf—it is a way such calves have.

Thus it is with our modern paganism. We all of us want to be idealists, and we sometimes try, but there are hidden causes which draw us back again to the earth. These causes lie in the opportunities that occur one by one: in politics, in industrial and commercial matters, in scientific theories, or by mere reaction. The earth is more habitable than once it was, and we all desire it. It masters us, and so the golden calf appears.

We shall now glance very rapidly at a few out of the many literary forces of our day in which we may see the various reactions from Carlyle. First, there was the Early Victorian time, the eighteenth century in homespun. It was not great and pompous like that century, but it lived by formality, propriety, and conventionality. It was horribly shocked when George Eliot published *Scenes of Clerical Life* and *Adam Bede* in 1858 and 1859. Outwardly it was eminently respectable, and its respectablity was its particular method of lapsing into paganism. It was afraid of ideals, and for those who cherish this fear the worship of respectablity comes to be a very dangerous kind of worship, and its idol is perhaps the most formidable of all the gods.

Meanwhile that glorious band of idealists, whose chief representatives were Tennyson, Browning, and Ruskin, to be joined later by George Meredith, were fighting paganism in the spirit of Arthur's knights, keen to drive the heathen from the land. Tennyson, the most popular of them all, probably achieved more than any other in this conflict. Ruskin was too contradictory and bewildering, and so failed of much of his effect. Browning and Meredith at first were reckoned unintelligible, and had to wait their day for a later understanding. Still, all these, and many others of lesser power than theirs, were knights of the ideal, warring against the domination of dead and unthinking respectability.

Matthew Arnold came upon the scene, with his great protest against the preponderance of single elements in life, and his plea for wholeness. In this demand for whole and not one-sided views of the world, he is more nearly akin to Goethe than perhaps any other writer of our time. His great protest was against the worship of machinery, which he believed to be taking the place of its own productions in England. He conceived of the English people as being under a general delusion which led them to mistake means for ends. He spoke of them as "Barbarians, Philistines, and

Populace," according to the rank in life they held; and accused them of living for such ends as field sports, the disestablishment of the Church of England, and the drinking of beer. He pointed out that, so far as real culture is concerned, these can at best be but means towards other ends, and can never be in themselves sufficient to satisfy the human soul. He protested against Carlyle, although in the main thesis the two are entirely at one. "I never liked Carlyle," he said; "he always seemed to me to be carrying coals to Newcastle." He took Carlyle for the representative of what he called "Hebraism," and he desired to balance the undue preponderance of that by insisting upon the necessity of the Hellenistic element in culture. Both of these are methods of idealism, but Arnold protested that the human spirit is greater than any of the forces that bear it onwards; and that after you have said all that Carlyle has to say, there still remains on the other side the intellect, with rights of its own. He did not exclude conscience, for he held that conduct made up three-fourths of life. He was the idealist of a whole culture as against all one-sidedness; but curiously, by flinging himself upon the opposite side from Carlyle, he became identified in the popular mind with what it imagined to be Hellenic paganism. This was partly due to his personal idiosyncrasies, his fastidiousness of taste, and the somewhat cold style of the *exquisite* in expression. These deceived many of his readers, and kept them from seeing how great and prophetic a message it was that came to England beneath Arnold's mannerisms.

Dante Gabriel Rossetti appeared, and many more in his train. He, more perfectly than any other, expressed the marriage of sense and soul in modern English poetry. He was the idealist of emotion, who, in the far-off dim borderlands between sense and spirit, still preserved the spiritual search, nor ever allowed himself to be completely drugged with the vapours of the region. There were others, however, who tended towards decadence. Some of Rossetti's readers, whose sole interest lay in the lower world, claimed him as well as the rest for their guides, and set a fashion which is not yet obsolete. There is no lack of solemnity among these. The scent of sandalwood and of incense is upon their work, and you feel as you read them that you are worshipping in some sort of a temple with strange and solemnising rites. Indeed they insist upon this, and assiduously cultivate a kind of lethargic and quasi-religious manner which is supposed to be very impressive. But their temple is a pagan temple, and their worship, however much they may borrow for it the language of a more spiritual cult, is of the earth, earthy.

Mr. Thomas Hardy was the inevitable sequel to George Eliot. Everybody knows how beautiful and how full of charm his lighter writings can be; and in his more tragic work there is much that is true, terrifically expressed. Yet he has got upon the wrong side of the world, and can never see beyond the horror of its tragedy. Consequently in him we have another form of paganism, not this time that which the seductive earth with its charms is suggesting, but the hopeless paganism which sees the earth only in its bitterness. In *The Return of the Native* he says: "What the Greeks only suspected we know well; what their Aeschylus imagined our nursery children feel. That old-fashioned revelling in the general situation grows less and less possible as we uncover the defects of natural laws, and see the quandary man is in by their operation." It is no wonder that he who expressed the spirit of the modern age in these words should have closed his well-known novel with the bitter saying that the upper powers had finished their sport with *Tess*. "To have lost the God-like conceit that we may do what we will, and not to have acquired a homely zest for doing what we can, shows a grandeur of temper which cannot be objected to in the abstract, for it denotes a mind that, though disappointed, forswears compromise." Here is obviously a man who would love the highest if he saw it, who would fain welcome and proclaim the ideals if he could only find them on the earth; but who has found instead the bitterness of darkness, the sarcasm and the sensationalism of an age that the gods have left. He is too honest to shout *pour encourager les autres* when his own heart has no hope in it; and his greater books express the wail and despair of our modern paganism.

Breaking away from him and all such pessimistic voices came the glad soul of Robert Louis Stevenson, whose old-fashioned revelling in the situation is the exact counter-blast to Hardy's modernism, and is one of those perennial human things which are ever both new and old. It is not that Stevenson has not seen the other side of life. He has seen it and he has suffered from it deeply, both in himself and in others; yet still indomitably he "clings to his paddle." "I believe," he says, "in an ultimate decency of things; ay, and if I woke in hell, should still believe it."

Then there came the extraordinary spirit of Mr. Rudyard Kipling. At first sight some things that he has written appear pagan enough, and have been regarded as such. The God of Christians seems to inhabit and preside over an amazing Valhalla of pagan divinities; and indeed throughout Mr. Kipling's work the heavens and the earth are mingled in a most inextricable and astonishing fashion. It is said that not long ago, during the launch of a Chinese battleship at one of our British yards, they were burning papers to the gods in a small joss-house upon the pier, while the great vessel, fitted with all the most modern machinery, was leaving the stocks. There is something about the tale that reminds us of Mr. Kipling. Now he is the prophet of Jehovah, now the Corybantic pagan priest, now the interpreter of the soul of machines. He is everything and everybody. He knows the heart of the unborn, and, telling of days far in the future, can make them as living and real as the hours of to-day. It was the late Professor James who said of him, "Kipling is elemental; he is down among the roots of all things. He is universal like the sun. He is at home everywhere. When he dies they won't be able to get any grave to hold him. They will have to bury him under a pyramid." In our reckoning such a man hardly counts. It would be most interesting, if it were as yet possible, to speculate as to whether his permanent influence has been more on the side of a kind of a wild Titanic paganism, or of that ancient

Calvinistic God whom Macandrew worships in the temple of his engine-room.

We now come to a later phase, for which we may take as representative writers the names of Mr. H. G. Wells and Mr. Bernard Shaw. Science, for the meantime at least, has disentangled herself from her former materialism, and a nobly ideal and spiritual view of science has come again. It may even be hoped that the pagan view will never be able again to assert itself with the same impressiveness as in the past. But social conditions are to-day in the throes of their strife, and from that quarter of the stage there appear such writers as those we are now to consider. They both present themselves as idealists. Mr. Wells has published a long volume about his religion, and Mr. Shaw prefaces his plays with essays as long or even longer than the plays themselves, dealing with all manner of the most serious subjects. The surface flippancy both of prefaces and plays has repelled some readers in spite of all their cleverness, and tended towards an unjust judgment that he is upsetting the universe with his tongue in his cheek all the time. Later one comes to realise that this is not the case, that Mr. Shaw does really take himself and his message seriously, and from first to last conceives himself as the apostle of a tremendous creed. Among many other things which they have in common, these writers have manifested the tendency to regard all who ever went before them as, in a certain sense, thieves and robbers; at least they give one the impression that the present has little need for long lingering over the past. Mr. Wells, for instance, cannot find words strong enough to describe the emancipation of the modern young man from Mr. Kipling with his old-fashioned injunction, "Keep ye the law." There are certain laws which Mr. Wells proclaims on the housetops that he sees no necessity for keeping, and so Mr. Kipling is buried under piles of opprobrium—"the tumult and the bullying, the hysteria and the impatience, the incoherence and the inconsistency," and so on. As for Mr. Bernard Shaw, we all know his own view of the relation in which he stands to William Shakespeare.

Mr. Wells has written many interesting books, and much could be said of him from the point of view of science, or of style, or of social theory. That, however, is not our present concern, either with him or with Mr. Shaw. It is as idealist or pagan influences that we are discussing them and the others. Mr. Wells boasts a new morality in his books, and Mr. Shaw in his plays. One feels the same startling sense of a *volte face* in morality as a young recruit is said to do when he finds all the precepts of his childhood reversed by the ethics of his first battlefield. Each in his own way falls back upon crude and primitive instincts and justifies them.[1]

Mr. Wells takes the change with zest, and seems to treat the adoption of a new morality in the same light-hearted spirit as he might consider the buying of a new hat. From the first he has a terrifying way of dealing familiarly with vast things. Somehow he reminds one of those jugglers who, for a time, toss heavy balls about, and then suddenly astonish the audience by introducing a handkerchief, which flies lightly among its ponderous companions. So Mr. Wells began to juggle with worlds. He has latterly introduced that delicate thing, the human soul and conscience, into the play, and you see it precariously fluttering among the immensities of leaping planets. He persuades himself that the common morality has not gripped people, and that they really don't believe in it at all. He aims at a way of thinking which will be so great as to be free from all commonplace and convention. Honesty is to be

[1] In his latest volume (*Marriage*), Mr. Wells has spoken in a different tone from that of his other recent works. It is a welcome change, and it may be the herald of something more positive still, and of a wholesome and inspiring treatment of the human problems. But behind it lie *First and Last Things*, *Tono Bungay*, *Ann Veronica*, and *The New Macchiavelli*.

practically the only virtue in the new world. If you say what you mean, you will earn the right to do anything else that you please. Mr. Wells in this is the counterpart of those plain men in private life so well known to us all, who perpetually remind us that they are people who call a spade a spade. Such men are apt to interpret this dictum as a kind of charter which enables a man to say anything foolish, or rude, or bad that may occur to him, and earn praise for it instead of blame. Some of us fail to find the greatness of this way of thinking, however much we may be impressed by its audacity. Indeed there seems to be much smallness in it which masquerades as immensity.

This smallness is due first of all to sheer ignorance. When a man tells us that he prefers Oliver Goldsmith to Jesus Christ, he merely shows that upon the subject he is discussing he is not educated, and does not know what he is talking about. A second source of pettiness is to be found in the mistake of imagining that mere smartness of diction and agility of mind are signs of intellectual keenness. The mistake is as obvious as it is unfortunate. Smartness can be learned with perhaps the least expenditure of intellect that is demanded by any literary exercise of the present day. It is a temptation which a certain kind of clever man always has to face, and it only assumes a serious aspect when it leads the unthinking to mistake it for a new and formidable element of opposition to things which he has counted sacred.

The whole method is not so very subtle after all. Pick out a vice or a deformity. Do not trouble to acquaint yourself too intimately with the history of morals in the past, but boldly canonise your vice or your deformity with ritual of epigram and paradox. Proclaim loudly and eloquently that this is your faith, and give it a pathetic aspect by dwelling tenderly upon any trouble which it may be likely to cost those who venture to adopt it. It is not perhaps a very admirable way to deal with such subjects. The whole world of tradition and the whole constitution of human nature are against you. Men have wrestled with these things for thousands of years, and they have come to certain conclusions which the experience of all time has enforced upon them. By a dash of bold imagination you may discount all that laborious past, and leave an irrevocable stain upon the purity of the mind of a generation. Doubtless you will have a following—such teachers have ever had those who followed them—and yet time is always on the side of great traditions. If enlightened thought has in any respect to change them, it changes them reverently, and knowing what their worth has been. Sooner or later all easy ignoring of them is condemned as sheer impertinence. There is singularly little reason for being impressed by this hasty, romantic, and loud-sounding crusade against Christian morality and its Ideal.

In Mr. George Bernard Shaw we have a very different man. Nobody denies Mr. Shaw's cleverness, least of all Mr. Shaw himself. He is depressingly clever. He exhibits the spectacle of a man trying to address his audience while standing on his head —and succeeding.

He has been singularly fortunate in his biographer, Mr. Chesterton, and one of the things that make this biography such pleasing reading is the personal element that runs through it all. The introduction is characteristic and delightful: "Most people either say that they agree with Bernard Shaw, or that they do not understand him. I am the only person who understands him, and I do not agree with him." It is not unnatural that he should take his friend a little more seriously than most of us will be prepared to do. It really is a big thing to stand on the shoulders of William Shakespeare, and we shall need time to consider it before we subscribe to the statue.

For there is here an absolutely colossal egotism. There are certain newspapers which usually begin with a note of the hours of sunrise and sunset. During the recent coal strike, some of these newspapers inserted first of all a notice that they would not be sent out so early as usual, and then cheered our desponding hearts by assuring us that the sun rises at 5.37 notwithstanding—as if by permission of the newspaper. Mr. Shaw somehow gives us a similar impression. Most things in the universe seem to go on by his permission, and some of them he is not going to allow to go on much longer. He will tilt without the slightest vestige of humility against any existing institution, and the tourney is certainly one of the most entertaining and most extraordinary of our time.

No one can help admiring Mr. Shaw. The dogged persistence which has carried him, unflinching, through adversity into his present fame, without a single compromise or hesitation, is, apart altogether from the question of the truth of his opinions, an admirable quality in a man. We cannot but admire his immense forcefulness and agility, the fertility of his mind, and the swiftness of its play. But we utterly refuse to fall down and worship him on account of these. Indeed the kind of awe with which he is regarded in some quarters seems to be due rather to the eccentricities of his expression than to the greatness of his message or the brilliance of his achievements.

There is no question of his earnestness. The Puritan is deep in Mr. Shaw, in his very blood. He has indeed given to the term Puritan a number of unexpected meanings, and yet no one can justly question his right to it. His *Plays for Puritans* are not exceptional in this matter, for all his work is done in the same spirit. His favourite author is John Bunyan, about whom he tells us that he claims him as the precursor of Nietzsche, and that in his estimation John Bunyan's life was one long tilt against morality and respectability. The claim is sufficiently grotesque, yet there is a sense in which he has a right to John Bunyan, and is in the same line as Thomas Carlyle. He is trying sincerely to speak the truth and get it spoken. He appears as another of the destroyers of shams, the breakers of idols. He may indeed be claimed as a pagan, and his influence will certainly preponderate in that direction; and yet there is a strain of high idealism which runs perplexingly through it all.

The explanation seems to be, as Mr. Chesterton suggests, that the man is incomplete. There are certain elementary things which, if he had ever seen them as other people do, would have made many of his positions impossible. "Shaw is wrong," says Mr. Chesterton, "about nearly all the things one learns early in life while one is still simple." Among those things which he has never seen are the loyalties involved in love, country, and religion. The most familiar proof of this in regard to religion is his extraordinary tirade against the Cross of Calvary. It is one of the most amazing passages in print, so far as either taste or judgment is concerned. It is significant that in this very passage he actually refers to the "stable at Bethany," and the slip seems to indicate from what a distance he is discussing Christianity. It is possible for any of us to measure himself against the Cross and Him who hung upon it, only when we have travelled very far away from them. When we are sufficiently near, we know ourselves to be infinitesimal in comparison. Nor in regard to home, and all that sanctifies and defends it, does Mr. Shaw seem ever to have understood the real morality that is in the heart of the average man. The nauseating thing which he quotes as morality is a mere caricature of that vital sense of honour and imperative conscience of righteousness which, thank God, are still alive among us. "My dear," he says, "you are the incarnation of morality, your conscience is clear and your duty done when you have called everybody names." Similar, and no less unfortunate, is his perversion of that instinct of patriotism which, however mistaken in some of its expressions, has yet proved its moral and practical worth during many a century of British history. There is the less need to dwell upon this, because those who discard patriotism have only to state their case clearly in order to discredit it.

We do not fear greatly the permanent influence of these fundamental errors. The great heart of the civilised world still beats true, and is healthy enough to disown so maimed an account of human nature. Yet there is danger in any such element in literature as this. Mr. Shaw's biographer has virtually told us that in these matters he is but a child in whom "Irish innocence is peculiar and fundamental." The pleadings of the nurse for the precocious and yet defective infant are certainly very touching. He may be the innocent creature that Mr. Chesterton takes him for, but he has said things which will exactly suit the views of libertines who read him. Such pleadings are quite unavailing to exeuse any such child if he does too much innocent mischief. His puritanism and his childlikeness only make his teaching more dangerous because more piquant. It has the air of proceeding from the same source as the ten commandments, and the effect of this upon the unreflecting is always considerable. If a child is playing in a powder magazine, the more childish and innocent he is the more dangerous he will prove; and the explosion, remember, will be just as violent if lit by a child's hand as if it had been lit by an anarchist's. We have in England borne long enough with people trifling with the best intentions among explosives, moral and social, and we must consider our own safety and that of society when we are judging them.

As to the relation in which Mr. Shaw stands to paganism, his relations to anything are so "extensive and peculiar" that they are always difficult to define. But the later phase of his work, which has become famous in connection with the word "Superman," is due in large part to Nietzsche, whose strange influence has reversed the Christian ideals for many disciples on both sides of the North Sea. So this idealist, who, in *Major Barbara*, protests so vigorously against paganism, has become one of its chief advocates and expositors. One of his characters somewhere says, "I wish I could get a country to live in where the facts were not brutal and the dreams were not unreal." It may be admitted that there are many brutal facts and perhaps more unreal dreams; but, for our part, that which keeps us from becoming pagans is that we have found facts that are not brutal and dreams which are the realest things in life.

LECTURE IX

MR. G. K. CHESTERTON'S POINT OF VIEW

THERE is on record the case of a man who, after some fourteen years of robust health, spent a week in bed. His illness was apparently due to a violent cold, but he confessed, on medical cross-examination, that the real and underlying cause was the steady reading of Mr. Chesterton's books for several days on end.

No one will accuse Mr. Chesterton of being an unhealthy writer. On the contrary, he is among the most wholesome writers now alive. He is irresistibly exhilarating, and he inspires his readers with a constant inclination to rise up and shout. Perhaps his danger lies in that very fact, and in the exhaustion of the nerves which such sustained exhilaration is apt to produce. But besides this, he, like so many of our contemporaries, has written such a bewildering quantity of literature on such an amazing variety of subjects, that it is no wonder if sometimes the reader follows panting, through the giddy mazes of the dance. He is the sworn enemy of specialisation, as he explains in his remarkable essay on "The Twelve Men." The subject of the essay is the British jury, and its thesis is that when our civilisation "wants a library to be catalogued, or a solar system discovered, or any trifle of that kind, it uses up its specialists. But when it wishes anything done which is really serious, it collects twelve of the ordinary men standing round. The same thing was done, if I remember right, by the Founder of Christianity." For the judging of a criminal or the propagation of the gospel, it is necessary to procure inexpert people—people who come to their task with a virgin eye, and see not what the expert (who has lost his freshness) sees, but the human facts of the case. So Mr. Chesterton insists upon not being a specialist, takes the world for his parish, and wanders over it at will.

This being so, it is obvious that he cannot possibly remember all that he has said, and must necessarily abound in inconsistencies and even contradictions. Yet that is by no means always unconscious, but is due in many instances to the very complex quality and subtle habit of his mind. Were he by any chance to read this statement he would deny it fiercely, but we would repeat it with perfect calmness, knowing that he would probably have denied any other statement we might have made upon the subject. His subtlety is partly due to the extraordinary rapidity with which his mind leaps from one subject to another, partly to the fact that he is so full of ideas that many of his essays (like Mr. Bernard Shaw's plays) find it next to impossible to get themselves begun. He is so full of matter that he never seems to be able to say what he wants to say, until he has said a dozen other things first.

The present lecture is mainly concerned with his central position, as that is expounded in *Heretics* and *Orthodoxy*. Our task is not to criticise, nor even to any considerable extent to characterise his views, but to state them as accurately as we can. It is a remarkable phenomenon of our time that all our literary men are bent on giving us such elaborate and solemnising confessions of their faith. It is an age notorious for its aversion to dogma, and yet here we have Mr. Huxley, Mr. Le Gallienne, Mr. Shaw, Mr. Wells (to mention only a few of many), who in this creedless age proclaim in the market-place, each his own private and brand-new creed.

Yet Mr. Chesterton has perhaps a special right to such a proclamation. He believes in creeds vehemently. And, besides, the spiritual biography of a man whose mental development has been so independent and so interesting as his, must be well worth knowing. Amid the many weird theologies of our time we have met with nothing so startling, so arresting, and so suggestive since Mr. Mallock published his *New Republic* and his *Contemporary Superstitions*. There is something common to the two points of view. To some, they come as emancipating and most welcome reinforcements, relieving the beleaguered citadel of faith. But others, who differ widely from them both, may yet find in them so much to stimulate thought and to rehabilitate strongholds held precariously, as to awaken both appreciation and gratitude.

Mr. Chesterton's political opinions do not concern us here. It is a curious fact, of which innumerable illustrations may be found in past and present writers, that political radicalism so often goes along with conservative theology, and *vice versa*. Mr. Chesterton is no exception to the rule. His orthodoxy in matters of faith we shall find to be altogether above suspicion. His radicalism in politics is never long silent. He openly proclaims himself at war with Carlyle's favourite dogma, "The tools to him who can use them." "The worst form of slavery," he tells us, "is that which is called Cæsarism, or the choice of some bold or brilliant man as despot because he is suitable. For that means that men choose a representative, not because he represents them but because he does not." And if it be answered that the worst form of cruelty to a nation or to an individual is that abuse of the principle of equality which is for ever putting incompetent people into false positions, he has his reply ready: "The one specially and peculiarly un-Christian idea is the idea of Carlyle—the idea that the man should rule who feels that he can rule. Whatever else is Christian, this is heathen."

But this, and much else of its kind, although he works it into his general scheme of thinking, is not in any sense an essential part of that scheme. Our subject is his place in the conflict between the paganism and the idealism of the times, and it is a sufficiently large one. But before we come to that, we must consider another matter, which we shall find to be intimately connected with it.

That other matter is his habit of paradox, which is familiar to all his readers. It is a habit of style, but before it became that it was necessarily first a habit of mind, deeply ingrained. He disclaims it so often that we cannot but feel that he protesteth too much. He acknowledges it, and explains that "paradox simply means a certain defiant joy which belongs to belief." Whether the explanation is or is not perfectly intelligible, it must occur to every one that a writer who finds it necessary to give so remarkable an explanation can hardly be justified in his astonishment when people of merely average intelligence confess themselves puzzled. His aversion to Walter Pater—almost the only writer whom he appears consistently to treat with disrespect—is largely due to Pater's laborious simplicity of style. But it was a greater than either Walter Pater or Mr. Chesterton who first pointed out that the language which appealed to the understanding of the common man was also that which expressed the highest culture. Mr. Chesterton's habit of paradox will always obscure his meanings for the common man. He has a vast amount to tell him, but much of it he will never understand.

Paradox, when it has become a habit, is always dangerous. Introduced on rare and fitting occasions, it may be powerful and even convincing, but when it is repeated constantly and upon all sorts of subjects, we cannot but dispute its right and question its validity. Its effect is not conviction but vertigo. It is like trying to live in a house constructed so as to be continually turning upside down. After a certain time, during which terror and dizziness alternate, the most indulgent reader is apt to turn round upon the builder of such a house with some asperity. And, after all, the general judgment may be right and Mr. Chesterton wrong.

Upon analysis, his paradox reveals as its chief and most essential element a certain habit of mind which always tends to see and appreciate the reverse of accepted opinions. So much is this the case that it is possible in many instances to anticipate what he will say upon a subject. It is on record that one reader, coming to his chapter on Omar Khayyám, said to himself, "Now he will be saying that Omar is not drunk enough"; and he went on to read, "It is not poetical drinking, which is joyous and instinctive; it is rational drinking, which is as prosaic as an investment, as unsavoury as a dose of camomile." Similarly we are told that Browning is only felt to be obscure because he is too pellucid. Such apparent contradictoriness is everywhere in his work, but along with it goes a curious ingenuity and nimbleness of mind. He cannot think about anything without remembering something else, apparently out of all possible connection with it, and instantly discovering some clever idea, the introduction of which will bring the two together. Christianity "is not a mixture like russet or purple; it is rather like a shot silk, for a shot silk is always at right angles, and is in the pattern of the cross."

In all this there are certain familiar mechanisms which constitute almost a routine of manipulation for the manufacture of paradoxes. One such mechanical process is the play with the derivatives of words. Thus he reminds us that the journalist is, in the literal and derivative sense, a *journalist*, while the missionary is an eternalist. Similarly "lunatic," "evolution," "progress," "reform," are etymologically tortured into the utterance of the most forcible and surprising truths. This curious word-play was a favourite method with Ruskin; and it has the disadvantage in Mr. Chesterton which it had in the earlier critic. It appears too clever to be really sound, although it must be confessed that it frequently has the power of startling us into thoughts that are valuable and suggestive.

Another equally simple process is that of simply reversing sentences and ideas. "A good bush needs no wine." "Shakespeare (in a weak moment, I think) said that all the world is a stage. But Shakespeare acted on the much finer principle that a stage is all the world." Perhaps the most brilliant example that could be quoted is the plea for the combination of gentleness and ferocity in Christian character. When the lion lies down with the lamb, it is constantly assumed that the lion becomes lamblike. "But that is brutal annexation and imperialism on the part of the lamb. That is simply the lamb absorbing the lion, instead of the lion eating the lamb."

By this process it is possible to attain results which are extraordinarily brilliant in themselves and fruitful in suggestion. It is a process not difficult to learn, but the trouble is that you have to live up to it afterwards, and defend many curious propositions which may have been arrived at by its so simple means. Take, for instance, the sentence about the stage being all the world. That is undeniably clever, and it contains an idea. But it is a haphazard idea, arrived at by a short-cut, and not by the high road of reasonable thinking. Sometimes a truth may be reached by such a short-cut, but such paradoxes are occasionally no better than chartered errors.

Yet even when they are that, it may be said in their favour that they startle us into thought. And truly Mr. Chesterton is invaluable as a quickener and stimulator of the minds of his readers. Moreover, by adopting the method of paradox, he has undoubtedly done one remarkable thing.

He has proved what an astonishing number of paradoxical surprises there actually are, lying hidden beneath the apparent commonplace of the world. Every really clever paradox astonishes us not merely with the sense of the cleverness of him who utters it, but with the sense of how many strange coincidences exist around us, and how many sentences, when turned outside in, will yield new and startling truths. However much we may suspect that the performance we are watching is too clever to be trustworthy, yet after all the world does appear to lend itself to such treatment.

There is, for example, the paradox of the love of the world—"Somehow one must love the world without being worldly." Again, "Courage is almost a contradiction in terms. It means a strong desire to live taking the form of a readiness to die." The martyr differs from the suicide in that he cherishes a disdain of death, while the motive of the suicide is a disdain of life. Charity, too, is a paradox, for it means "one of two things—pardoning unpardonable acts, or loving unlovable people." Similarly Christian humility has a background of unheard-of arrogance, and Christian liberty is possible only to the most abject bondsmen in the world.

This long consideration of Mr. Chesterton's use of paradox is more relevant to our present subject than it may seem. For, curiously enough, the habit of paradox has been his way of entrance into faith. At the age of sixteen he was a complete agnostic, and it was the reading of Huxley and Herbert Spencer and Bradlaugh which brought him back to orthodox theology. For, as he read, he found that Christianity was attacked on all sides, and for all manner of contradictory reasons; and this discovery led him to the conviction that Christianity must be a very extraordinary thing, abounding in paradox. But he had already discovered the abundant element of paradox in life; and when he analysed the two sets of paradoxes he found them to be precisely the same. So he became a Christian.

It may seem a curious way to enter the Kingdom of Heaven. Those who are accustomed to regard the strait gate as of Gothic architecture may be shocked to find a man professing to have entered through this Alhambra-like portal. But it is a lesson we all have to learn sooner or later, that there are at least eleven gates besides our own, and that every man has to enter by that which he finds available. Paradox is the only gate by which Mr. Chesterton could get into any place, and the Kingdom of Heaven is no exception to the rule.

His account of this entrance is characteristic. It is given in the first chapter of his *Orthodoxy*.

There was an English yachtsman who set out upon a voyage, miscalculated his course, and discovered what he thought to be a new island in the South Seas. It transpired afterwards that he had run up his flag on the pavilion of Brighton, and that he had discovered England. That yachtsman is Mr. Chesterton himself. Sailing the great sea of moral and spiritual speculation, he discovered a land of facts and convictions to which his own experience had guided him. On that strange land he ran up his flag, only to make the further and more astonishing discovery that it was the Christian faith at which he had arrived. Nietzsche had preached to him, as to Mr. Bernard Shaw, his great precept, "Follow your own will." But when Mr. Chesterton obeyed he arrived, not at Superman, but at the ordinary old-fashioned morality. That, he found, is what we like best in our deepest hearts, and desire most. So he too "discovered England."

He begins, like Margaret Fuller, with the fundamental principle of accepting the universe. The thing we know best and most directly is human nature in all its breadth. It is indeed the one thing immediately known and knowable. Like R. L. Stevenson, he perceives how tragically and comically astonishing a phenomenon is man. "What a monstrous spectre is this man," says Stevenson, "the disease of the agglutinated dust, lifting alternate feet or lying drugged with slumber; killing, feeding, growing, bringing forth small copies of himself; grown upon with hair like grass, fitted with eyes that move and glitter in his face; a thing to set children screaming;—and yet looked at nearlier, known as his fellows know him, how surprising are his attributes!" In like manner Mr. Chesterton discovers man — that appalling mass of paradox and contradiction — and it is the supreme discovery in any spiritual search.

Having discovered the fundamental fact of human nature, he at once gives in his allegiance to it. "Our attitude towards life can be better expressed in terms of a kind of military loyalty than in terms of criticism and approval. My acceptance of the universe is not optimism, it is more like patriotism. It is a matter of primary loyalty. The world is not a lodging-house at Brighton, which we are to leave because it is miserable. It is the fortress of our family, with the flag flying on the turret, and the more miserable it is, the less we should leave it."

There is a splendid courage and heartiness in his complete acceptance of life and the universe. In a time when clever people are so busy criticising life that they are in danger of forgetting that they have to live it, so busy selecting such parts of it as suit their taste that they ignore the fact that the other parts are there, he ignores nothing and wisely accepts instead of criticising. Mr. Bernard Shaw, as we have seen, will consent to tolerate the universe *minus* the three loyalties to the family, the nation, and God. Mr. Chesterton has no respect whatever for any such mutilated scheme of human life. His view of the institution of the family is full of wholesome common sense. He perceives the immense difficulties that beset all family life, and he accepts them with immediate and unflinching loyalty, as essential parts of our human task. His views on patriotism belong to the region of politics and do not concern us here. In regard to religion, he finds the modern school amalgamating everything in characterless masses of generalities. They deny the reality of sin, and in matters of faith generally they have put every question out of focus until the whole picture is blurred and vague. He attacks this way of dealing with religion in one of his most amusing essays, "The Orthodox Barber." The barber has been sarcastic about the new shaving—presumably in reference to M. Gillett's excellent invention. "'It seems you can shave yourself with anything—with a stick or a stone or a pole or a poker' (here I began for the first time to detect a sarcastic intonation) 'or a shovel or a——' Here he hesitated for a word, and I, although I knew nothing about the matter, helped him out with suggestions in the same rhetorical vein. 'Or a button-hook,' I said, 'or a blunderbuss or a battering-ram or a piston-rod——' He resumed, refreshed with this assistance, 'Or a curtain-rod or a candlestick or a——' 'Cow-catcher,' I suggested eagerly, and we continued in this ecstatic duet for some time. Then I asked him what it was all about, and he told me. He explained the thing eloquently and at length. 'The funny part of it is,' he said, 'that the thing isn't new at all. It's been talked about ever since I was a boy, and long before.'" Mr. Chesterton rejoins in a long and eloquent and most amusing sermon, the following extracts from which are not without far-reaching significance.

"'What you say reminds me in some dark and dreamy fashion of something else. I recall it especially when you tell me, with such evident experience and sincerity, that the new shaving is not really new. My friend, the human race is always trying this dodge of making everything entirely easy; but the difficulty which it shifts off one thing it shifts on to another. . . . It would be nice if we could be shaved without troubling anybody. It would be nicer still if we could go unshaved without annoying anybody—

"'But, O wise friend, chief Barber of the Strand,
Brother, nor you nor I have made the world.

Whoever made it, who is wiser, and we hope better than we, made it under strange limitations, and with painful conditions of pleasure. . . . But every now and then men jump up with the new something or other and say that everything can be had without sacrifice, that bad is good if you are only enlightened, and that there is no real difference between being shaved and not being shaved. The difference, they say, is only a difference of degree; everything is evolutionary and relative. Shavedness is immanent in man. . . . I have been profoundly interested in what you have told me about the New Shaving. Have you ever heard of a thing called the New Theology?' He smiled and said that he had not."

In contrast with all this, it is Mr. Chesterton's conviction that the facts must be unflinchingly and in their entirety accepted. With characteristic courage he goes straight to the root of the matter and begins with the fact of sin. "If it be true (as it certainly is) that a man can feel exquisite happiness in skinning a cat, then the religious philosopher can only draw one of two deductions. He must either deny the existence of God, as all atheists do; or he must deny the present union between God and man, as all Christians do. The new theologians seem to think it a highly rationalistic solution to deny the cat." It is as if he said, Here you have direct and unmistakable experience. A man knows his sin as he knows himself. He may explain it in either one way or another way. He may interpret the universe accordingly in terms either of heaven or of hell. But the one unreasonable and impossible thing to do is to deny the experience itself.

It is thus that he treats the question of faith all along the line. If you are going to be a Christian, or even fairly to judge Christianity, you must accept the whole of Christ's teaching, with all its contradictions, paradoxes, and the rest. Some men select his charity, others his social teaching, others his moral relentlessness, and so on, and reject all else. Each one of these aspects of the Christian faith is doubtless very interesting, but none of them by itself is an adequate representation of Christ. "They have torn the soul of Christ into silly strips, labelled egoism and altruism, and they are equally puzzled by His insane magnificence and His insane meekness. They have parted His garments among them, and for His vesture they have cast lots; though the coat was without seam, woven from the top throughout."

The characteristic word for Mr. Chesterton and his attitude to life is *vitality*. He has been seeking for human nature, and he has found it at last in

Christian idealism. But having found it, he will allow no compromise in its acceptance. It is life he wants, in such wholeness as to embrace every element of human nature. And he finds that Christianity has quickened and intensified life all along the line. It is the great source of vitality, come that men might have life and that they might have it more abundantly. He finds an essential joy and riot in creation, a "tense and secret festivity." And Christianity corresponds to that riot. "The more I considered Christianity, the more I found that while it had established a rule and order, the chief aim of that order was to give room for good things to run wild." It has let loose the wandering, masterless, dangerous virtues, and has insisted that not one or another of them shall run wild, but all of them together. The ideal of wholeness which Matthew Arnold so eloquently advocated, is not a dead mass of theories, but a world of living things. Christ will put a check on none of the really genuine elements in human nature. In Him there is no compromise. His love and His wrath are both burning. All the separate elements of human nature are in full flame, and it is the only ultimate way of peace and safety. The various colours of life must not be mixed but kept distinct. The red and white of passion and purity must not be blended into the insipid pink of a compromising and consistent respectability. They must be kept strong and separate, as in the blazing Cross of St. George on its shield of white.

Chaucer's "Daisy" is one of the greatest conceptions in all poetry. It has stood for centuries as the emblem of pure and priceless womanhood, with its petals of snowy white and its heart of gold. Mr. Chesterton once made a discovery that sent him wild with joy—

> "Then waxed I like the wind because of this,
> And ran like gospel and apocalypse
> From door to door, with wild, anarchic lips,
> Crying the very blasphemy of bliss."

The discovery was that "the Daisy has a ring of red." Purity is not the enemy of passion; nor must passion and purity be so toned down and blent with one another, as to give a neutral result. Both must remain, and both in full brilliance, the virgin white and the passionate blood-red ring.

In the present age of reason, the cry is all for tolerance, and for redefinition which will remove sharp contrasts and prove that everything means the same as everything else. In such an age a doctrine like this seems to have a certain barbaric splendour about it, as of a crusader risen from the dead. But Mr. Chesterton is not afraid of the consequences of his opinions. If rationalism opposes his presentation of Christianity, he will ride full tilt against reason. In recent years, from the time of Newman until now, there has been a recurring habit of discounting reason in favour of some other way of approach to truth and life. Certainly Mr. Chesterton's attack on reason is as interesting as any that have gone before it, and it is even more direct. Even on such a question as the problem of poverty he frankly prefers imagination to study. In art he demands instinctiveness, and has a profound suspicion of anybody who is conscious of possessing the artistic temperament. As a guide to truth he always would follow poetry in preference to logic. He is never tired of attacking rationality, and for him anything which is rationalised is destroyed in the process.

In one of his most provokingly unanswerable sallies, he insists that the true home of reason is the madhouse. "The madman is not the man who has lost his reason. The madman is the man who has lost everything except his reason." When we say that a man is mad, we do not mean that he is unable to conduct a logical argument. On the contrary, any one who knows madmen knows that they are usually most acute and ingeniously consistent in argument. They isolate some one fixed idea, and round that they build up a world that is fiercely and tremendously complete. Every detail fits in, and the world in which they live is not, as is commonly supposed, a world of disconnected and fantastic imaginations, but one of iron-bound and remorseless logic. No task is more humiliating, nor more likely to shake one's sense of security in fundamental convictions, than that of arguing out a thesis with a lunatic.

Further, beneath this rationality there is in the madman a profound belief in himself. Most of us regard with respect those who trust their own judgment more than we find ourselves able to trust ours. But not the most confident of them all can equal the unswerving confidence of a madman. Sane people never wholly believe in themselves. They are liable to be influenced by the opinion of others, and are willing to yield to the consensus of opinion of past or present thinkers. The lunatic cares nothing for the views of others. He believes in himself against the world, with a terrific grip of conviction and a faith that nothing can shake.

Mr. Chesterton applies his attack upon rationality to many subjects, with singular ingenuity. In the question of marriage and divorce, for instance, the modern school which would break loose from the ancient bonds can present their case with an apparently unassailable show of rationality. But his reply to them and to all other rationalists is that life is not rational and consistent but paradoxical and contradictory. To make life rational you have to leave out so many elements as to make it shrink from a big world to a little one, which may be complete, but can never be much of a world. Its conception of God may be a complete conception, but its God is not much of a God. But the world of human nature is a vast world, and the God of Christianity is an Infinite God. The huge mysteries of life and death, of love and sacrifice, of the wine of Cana and the Cross of Calvary — these outwit all logic and pass all understanding. So for sane men there comes in a higher authority. You may call it common sense, or mysticism, or faith, as you please. It is the extra element by virtue of which all sane thinking and all religious life are rendered possible. It is the secret spring of vitality alike in human nature and in Christian faith.

At this point it may be permissible to question Mr. Chesterton's use of words in one important point. He appears to fall into the old error of confounding reason with reasoning. Reason is one thing and argument another. It may be impossible to express either human nature or religious faith in a series of syllogistic arguments, and yet both may be reasonable in a higher sense. Reason includes those extra elements to which Mr. Chesterton trusts. It is the synthesis of our whole powers of finding truth. Many things which cannot be proved by reasoning may yet be given in reason —involved in any reasonable view of things as a whole. Thus faith includes reason—it *is* reason on a larger scale—and it is the only reasonable course for a man to take in a world of mysterious experience. If the matter were stated in that way, Mr. Chesterton would probably assent to it. Put crudely, the fashion of pitting faith against reason and discarding reason in favour of faith, is simply sawing off the branch on which you are sitting. The result is that you must fall to the ground at the feet of the sceptic, who asks, "How can you believe that which you have confessed there is no reason to believe?" We have abundant reason for our belief, and that reason includes those higher intuitions, that practical common sense, and that view of things as a whole, which the argument of the mere logician necessarily ignores.

With this reservation,[1] Mr. Chesterton's position in regard to faith is absolutely unassailable. He is the most vital of our modern idealists, and his peculiar way of thinking himself into his idealism has given to the term a richer and more spacious

[1] Mr. Chesterton perceives this, though he does not always express it unmistakably. He tells us that he does not mean to attack the authority of reason, but that his ultimate purpose is rather to defend it.

meaning, which combines excellently the Greek and the Hebrew elements. His great ideal is that of manhood. Be a man, he cries aloud, not an artist, not a reasoner, not any other kind or detail of humanity, but be a man. But then that means, Be a creature whose life swings far out beyond this world and its affairs—swings dangerously between heaven and hell. Eternity is in the heart of every man. The fashionable modern gospel of Pragmatism is telling us to-day that we should not vex ourselves about the ultimate truth of theories, but inquire only as to their value for life here and now, and the practical needs which they serve. But the most practical of all man's needs is his need of some contact with a higher world than that of sense. "To say that a man is an idealist is merely to say that he is a man." In the scale of differences between important and unimportant earthly things, it is the spiritual and not the material that counts. "An ignorance of the other world is boasted by many men of science; but in this matter their defect arises, not from ignorance of the other world, but from ignorance of this world." "The moment any matter has passed through the human mind it is finally and for ever spoilt for all purposes of science. It has become a thing incurably mysterious and infinite; this mortal has put on immortality."

Here we begin to see the immense value of paradox in the matter of faith. Mr. Chesterton is an optimist, not because he fits into this world, but because he does not fit into it. Pagan optimism is content with the world, and subsists entirely in virtue of its power to fit into it and find it sufficient. This is that optimism of which Browning speaks with scorn—

> "Tame in earth's paddock as her prize,"

and which he repudiates in the famous lines,

> "Then, welcome each rebuff
> That turns earth's smoothness rough,
> Each sting that bids nor sit nor stand but go!
> Be our joys three parts pain!
> Strive, and hold cheap the strain;
> Learn, nor account the pang; dare, never grudge the throe!"

Mr. Chesterton insists that beyond the things which surround us here on the earth there are other things which claim us from beyond. The higher instincts which discover these are not tools to be used for making the most of earthly treasures, but sacred relics to be guarded. He is an idealist who has been out beyond the world. There he has found a whole universe of mysterious but commanding facts, and has discovered that these and these alone can satisfy human nature.

The question must, however, arise, as to the validity of those spiritual claims. How can we be sure that the ideals which claim us from beyond are realities, and not mere dream shapes? There is no answer but this, that if we question the validity of our own convictions and the reality of our most pressing needs, we have simply committed spiritual suicide, and arrived prematurely at the end of all things. With the habit of questioning ultimate convictions Mr. Chesterton has little patience. Modesty, he tells us, has settled in the wrong place. We believe in ourselves and we doubt the truth that is in us. But we ourselves, the crude reality which we actually are, are altogether unreliable; while the vision is always trustworthy. We are for ever changing the vision to suit the world as we find it, whereas we ought to be changing the world to bring it into conformity with the unchanging vision. The very essence of orthodoxy is a profound and reverent conviction of ideals that cannot be changed—ideals which were the first, and shall be the last.

If Mr. Chesterton often strains his readers' powers of attention by rapid and surprising movements among very difficult themes, he certainly has charming ways of relieving the strain. The favourite among all such methods is his reversion to the subject of fairy tales. In "The Dragon's Grandmother" he introduces us to the arch-sceptic who did not believe in them—that fresh-coloured and short-sighted young man who had a curious green tie and a very long neck. It happened that this young man had called on him just when he had flung aside in disgust a heap of the usual modern problem-novels, and fallen back with vehement contentment on *Grimm's Fairy Tales.* "When he incidentally mentioned that he did not believe in fairy tales, I broke out beyond control. 'Man,' I said, 'who are you that you should not believe in fairy tales? It is much easier to believe in Blue Beard than to believe in you. A blue beard is a misfortune; but there are green ties which are sins. It is far easier to believe in a million fairy tales than to believe in one man who does not like fairy tales. I would rather kiss Grimm instead of a Bible and swear to all his stories as if they were thirty-nine articles than say seriously and out of my heart that there can be such a man as you; that you are not some temptation of the devil or some delusion from the void.'" The reason for this unexpected outbreak is a very deep one. "Folk-lore means that the soul is sane, but that the universe is wild and full of marvels. Realism means that the world is dull and full of routine, but that the soul is sick and screaming. The problem of the fairy tale is — what will a healthy man do with a fantastic world? The problem of the modern novel is—what will a madman do with a dull world? In the fairy tale the cosmos goes mad; but the hero does not go mad. In the modern novels the hero is mad before the book begins, and suffers from the harsh steadiness and cruel sanity of the cosmos."

In other words, the ideals, the ultimate convictions, are the trustworthy things; the actual experience of life is often matter not for distrust only but for scorn and contempt. And this philosophy Mr. Chesterton learned in the nursery, from that "solemn and star-appointed priestess," his nurse. The fairy tale, and not the problem-novel, is the true presentment of human nature and of life. For, in the first place it preserves in man the faculty most essential to human nature—the faculty of wonder, without which no man can live. To regain that faculty is to be born again, out of a false world into a true. The constant repetition of the laws of Nature blunts our spirits to the amazing character of every detail which she reproduces. To catch again the wonder of common things—

> "the hour
> Of splendour in the grass, of glory in the flower"

—is to pass from darkness into light, from falsehood to truth. "All the towering materialism which dominates the modern mind rests ultimately upon one assumption: a false assumption. It is supposed that if a thing goes on repeating itself it is probably dead: a piece of clockwork." But that is mere blindness to the mystery and surprise of everything that goes to make up actual human experience. "The repetition in Nature seemed sometimes to be an excited repetition, like that of an angry schoolmaster saying the same thing over and over again. The grass seemed signalling to me with all its fingers at once; the crowded stars seemed bent on being understood. The sun would make me see him if he rose a thousand times."

That is one fact, which fairy tales emphasise—the constant demand for wonder in the world, and the appropriateness and rightness of the wondering attitude of mind, as man passes through his lifelong gallery of celestial visions. The second fact is that all such vision is conditional, and "hangs upon a veto. All the dizzy and colossal things conceded depend upon one small thing withheld. All the wild and whirling things that are let loose depend upon one thing which is forbidden." This is the very note of fairyland. "You may live in a palace of gold and sapphire, *if* you do not say the word 'cow'; or you may live happily with the King's daughter, *if* you do not show her an onion." The conditions may seem arbitrary, but that is not the point. The point is that there always *are* conditions. The parallel with human life is obvious. Many people in the modern world are eagerly bent on having the reward without fulfilling the condition, but life is not made that way. The whole problem of marriage is a case in point. Its conditions are rigorous, and people on all sides are trying to relax them or to do away with them. Similarly, all along the line, modern society is seeking to live in a freedom which is in the nature of things incompatible with the enjoyment or the prosperity of the human spirit. There is an *if* in everything. Life is like that, and we cannot alter it. Quarrel with the seemingly arbitrary or unreasonable condition, and the whole fairy palace vanishes. "Life itself is as bright as the diamond, but as brittle as the window-pane."

From all this it is but a step to the consideration of dogma and the orthodox Christian creed. Mr. Chesterton is at war to the knife with vague modernism in all its forms. The eternal verities which produce great convictions are incomparably the most important things for human nature. No "inner light" will serve man's turn, but some outer light, and that only and always. "Christianity came into the world, firstly in order to assert with violence that a man had not only to look inwards, but to look outwards, to behold with astonishment and enthusiasm a divine company and a divine captain." This again is human nature. No man can live his life out fully without being mastered by convictions that he cannot challenge, and for whose origin he is not responsible. The most essentially human thing is the sense that these, the supreme conditions of life, are not of man's own arranging, but have been and are imposed upon him.

At almost every point this system may be disputed. Mr. Chesterton, who never shrinks from pressing his theories to their utmost length, scoffs at the modern habit of "saying that such-and-such a creed can be held in one age, but cannot be held in another. Some dogma, we are told, was credible in the twelfth century, but is not credible in the twentieth. You might as well say that a certain philosophy can be believed on Mondays, but cannot be believed on Tuesdays. You might as well say of a view of the cosmos that it was suitable to half-past three, but not suitable to half-past four." That is precisely what many of us do say. Our powers of dogmatising vary to some extent with our moods, and to a still greater extent with the reception of new light. There are many days on which the dogmas of early morning are impossible and even absurd when considered in the light of evening.

But it is not our task to criticise Mr. Chesterton's faith nor his way of dealing with it. Were we to do so, most of us would probably strike a balance. We would find many of his views and statements unconvincing; and yet we would acknowledge that they had the power of forcing the mind to see fresh truth upon which the will must act decisively. The main point in his orthodoxy is unquestionably a most valuable contribution to the general faith of his time and country. That point is the adventure which he narrates under the similitude of the voyage that ended in the discovery of England. He set out to find the empirical truth of human nature and the meaning of human life, as these are to be explored in experience. When he found them, it was infinitely surprising to him to become aware that the system in which his faith had come at last to rest was just Christianity—the only system which could offer any adequate and indeed exact account of human nature. The articles of its creed he recognised as the points of conviction which are absolutely necessary to the understanding of human nature and to the living of human life.

Thus it comes to pass that in the midst of a time resounding with pagan voices old and new, he stands for an unflinching idealism. It is the mark of pagans that they are children of Nature, boasting that Nature is their mother: they are solemnised by that still and unresponsive maternity, or driven into rebellion by discovering that the so-called mother is but a harsh stepmother after all. Mr. Chesterton loves Nature, because Christianity has revealed to him that she is but his sister, child of the same Father. "We can be proud of her beauty, since we have the same father; but she has no authority over us; we have to admire, but not to imitate."

It follows that two worlds are his, as is the case with all true idealists. The modern reversion to paganism is founded on the fundamental error that Christianity is alien to Nature, setting up against her freedom the repellent ideal of asceticism, and frowning upon her beauty with the scowl of the harsh moralist. For Mr. Chesterton the bleakness is all on the side of the pagans, and the beauty with the idealists. They do not look askance at the green earth at all. They gaze upon it with steady eyes, until they are actually looking through it, and discovering the radiance of heaven there, and the sublime brightness of the Eternal Life. The pagan virtues, such as justice and temperance, are painfully reasonable and often sad. The Christian virtues are faith, hope, and charity—each more unreasonable than the last, from the point of view of mere mundane common sense; but they are gay as childhood, and hold the secret of perennial youth and unfading beauty, in a world which upon any other terms than these is hastening to decay.

LECTURE X

THE HOUND OF HEAVEN

In bringing to a close these studies of the long battle between paganism and idealism,—between the life which is lived under the attraction of this world and which seeks its satisfaction there, and that wistful life of the spirit which has far thoughts and cannot settle down to the green and homely earth,—it is natural that we should look for some literary work which will describe the decisive issue of the whole conflict. Such a work is Francis Thompson's *Hound of Heaven*, which is certainly one of the most remarkable poems that have been published in England for many years.

To estimate its full significance it is necessary in a few words to recapitulate the course of thought which has been followed in the preceding chapters. We began with the ancient Greeks, and distinguished the high idealism of their religious conceptions from the paganism into which these declined. The sense of the sacredness of beauty, forced upon the Greek spirit by the earth itself, was a high idealism, without which no conception of life or of the universe can be anything but a maimed and incomplete expression of their meaning. Yet, for lack of some sufficiently powerful element of restraint and some sufficiently daring faith in spiritual reality, Hellenism sank back upon the mere earth, and its dying fires lit up a world too sordid for their sacred flame. In *Marius the Epicurean* the one thing lacking was supplied by the faith of early Christianity. The Greek idealism of beauty was not only conserved but enriched, and the human spirit was revived, by that heroic faith which endured as seeing the invisible. The two *Fausts* revealed the struggle at later stages of the development of Christianity. Marlowe's showed it under the light of mediæval theology and Goethe's under that of modern humanism, with the curious result that in the former tragedy the man is the pagan and the devil the idealist, while in the latter this order is reversed. Omar Khayyám and Fiona Macleod introduce the Oriental and the Celtic strains. In both there is the cry of the senses and the strong desire and allurement of the green carth; but in Fiona Macleod there is the dominant undertone of the eternal and the spiritual, never silent and finally overwhelming.

The next two lectures, in a cross-section of the

seventeenth century, showed John Bunyan keenly alive to the literature and the life of the world of Charles the Second's time, yet burning straight flame of spiritual idealism with these for fuel. Over against him stood Samuel Pepys, lusty and most amusing, declaring in every page of his *Diary* the lengths to which unblushing paganism can go.

Representative of modern literature, Carlyle comes first with his *Sartor Resartus.* At the ominous and uncertain beginning of our modern thought he stood, blowing loud upon his iron trumpet a great blast of harsh but grand idealism, before which the walls of the pagan Jericho fell down in many places. Yet such an inspiring challenge as his was bound to produce *reactions*, and we have them in many forms. Matthew Arnold presses upon his time, in clear and unimpassioned voice, the claim of neglected Hellenism. Rossetti, with heavy, half-closed eyes, hardly distinguishes the body from the soul. Mr. Thomas Hardy, the Titan of the modern world, whose heart is sore with disillusion and the bitterness of the earth, and yet blind to the light of heaven that still shines upon it, has lived into the generation which is reading Mr. Wells and Mr. Shaw. These appear to be outside of all such distinctions as pagan and idealist; but their influence is strongly on the pagan side. Mr.

Chesterton appears, with his quest of human nature, and he finds it not on earth but in heaven. He is the David of Christian faith, come to fight against the heretic Goliaths of his day; and, so far as his style and literary manner go, he continues the ancient rôle, smiting Goliath with his own sword.

Francis Thompson's *Hound of Heaven* is for many reasons a fitting close and climax to these studies. He is as much akin to Shelley and Swinburne as Mr. Chesterton is akin to Mr. Bernard Shaw. From them he has gathered not a little of his style and diction. He is with them, too, in his passionate love of beauty, without which no idealist can possibly be a fair judge of paganism. "With many," he tells us in that *Essay on Shelley* which Mr. Wyndham pronounces the most important contribution to English letters during the last twenty years—"with many the religion of beauty must always be a passion and a power, and it is only evil when divorced from the worship of the Primal Beauty." In this confession we are brought back to the point where we began. The gods of Greece were ideals of earthly beauty, and by them, while their worship remained spiritual, men were exalted far above paganism. And now, as we are drawing to a close, it is fitting that we should again remind ourselves that religious idealism must recover "the Christ beautiful," if it is to retain its hold upon humanity. In this respect, religion has greatly and disastrously failed, and he who can redeem that failure for us will indeed be a benefactor to his race. Religion should lead us not merely to inquire in God's holy place, but to behold the beauty of the Lord; and to behold it in all places of the earth until they become holy places for us. Christ, the Man of Sorrows, has taught the world that wild joy of which Mr. Chesterton speaks such exciting things. It remains for Thompson to remind us that he whose visage was more marred than any man yet holds that secret of surpassing beauty after which the poets' hearts are seeking so wistfully.

Besides all this, we shall find here something which has not as yet been hinted at in our long quest. The sound of the age-long battle dies away. Here is a man who does not fight for any flag, but simply tells us the mysterious story of his own soul and ours. It is a quiet and a fitting close for our long tale of excursions and alarums. But into the quiet ending there enters a very wonderful and exciting new element. We have been watching successive men following after the ideal, which, like some receding star, travelled before its pilgrims through the night. Here the ideal is no longer passive, a thing to be pursued.

It halts for its pilgrims—"the star which chose to stoop and stay for us." Nay, more, it turns upon them and pursues them. The ideal is alive and aware—a real and living force among the great forces of the universe. It is out after men, and in this great poem we are to watch it hunting a soul down. The whole process of idealism is now suddenly reversed, and the would-be captors of celestial beauty are become its captives.

As has been already stated, we must be in sympathetic understanding with the pagan heart in order to be of any account as advocates of idealism. No reader of Thompson's poetry can doubt for a moment his fitness here. From the days of Pindar there has been a brilliant succession of singers and worshippers of the sun, culminating in the matchless song of Shelley. In Francis Thompson's poems of the sun, the succession is taken up again in a fashion which is not unworthy of the splendours of paganism at its very highest.

"And the sun comes with power amid the clouds of heaven,
Before his way
Went forth the trumpet of the March
Before his way, before his way,
Dances the pennon of the May!
O Earth, unchilded, widowed Earth, so long
Lifting in patient pine and ivy-tree
Mournful belief and steadfast prophecy,
Behold how all things are made true!
Behold your bridegroom cometh in to you
Exceeding glad and strong!"

The great song takes us back to the days of Mithra and the *sol invictus* of Aurelian. That outburst of sunshine in the evening of the Roman Empire, rekindling the fires of Apollo's ancient altars for men who loved the sunshine and felt the wonder of it, is repeated with almost added glory in Thompson's marvellous poems.

Yet for Francis Thompson all this glory of the sun is but a symbol. The world where his spirit dwells is beyond the sun, and in nature it displays itself to man but brokenly. In the bloody fires of sunset, in the exquisite white artistry of the snow-flake, this supernatural world is but showing us a few of its miracles, by which the miracles of Christian faith are daily and hourly matched for sheer wonder and beauty. The idealist claims as his inheritance all those things in which the pagan finds his gods, and views them as the revelations of the Master Spirit.

It is difficult to write about Thompson's poetry without writing mainly about himself. In *The Hound of Heaven*, as in much else that he has written, there is abundance of his own experience, and indeed his poems often remind us of the sorrows of Teufelsdröckh. That, however, is not the purpose of this lecture; and, beyond a few notes of a general kind, we shall leave him to reveal himself. Except for Mr. Meynell's illuminative and all too short introduction to his volume of *Thompson's Selected Poems*, there are as yet only scattered articles in magazines to tell his strange and most pathetic story. His writings are few, comprising three short books of poetry, his prose *Essay on Shelley*, and a *Life of St. Ignatius*, which is full of interest and almost overloaded with information, but which may be discounted from the list of his permanent contributions to literature or to thought. Yet that small output is enough to establish him among the supreme poets of our land.

Apart from its poetic power and spiritual vision, his was an acute and vivid mind. On things political and social he could express himself in little casual flashes whose shrewd and trenchant incisiveness challenge comparison with Mr. Chesterton's own asides. His acquaintance with science seems to have been extensive, and at times he surprises us with allusions and metaphors of an unusually technical kind, which he somehow renders intelligible even to the non-scientific reader. These are doubly illuminative, casting spiritual light on the material world, and strengthening with material fact the tenuous thoughts of the spiritual. The words which he used of Shelley are, in this respect, applicable to himself. "To Shelley's ethereal vision the most rarefied mental or spiritual music traced its beautiful corresponding forms on the sand of outward things."

His style and choice of words are an achievement in themselves, as distinctive as those of Thomas Carlyle. They, and the attitude of mind with which they are congruous, have already set a fashion in our poetry, and some of its results are excellent. In *Rose and Vine*, and in other poems of Mrs. Rachel Annand Taylor, we have the same blend of power and beauty, the same wildness in the use of words, and the same languor and strangeness as if we had entered some foreign and wonderfully coloured world. In *Ignatius* the style and diction are quite simple, ordinary, and straightforward, but that biography is decidedly the least effective of his works. It would seem that here as elsewhere among really great writings the style is the natural and necessary expression of the individual mind and imagination. The *Life of Shelley*, which is certainly one of the masterpieces of English prose, has found for its expression a style quite unique and distinctive, in which there are constant reminders of other stylists, yet no imitation of any. The poetry is drugged, and as we read his poems through in the order of their publication, we feel the power of the poppy more and more. At last the hand seems to lose its power and the will its control, though in flashes of sheer flame the imagination shows wild and beautiful as ever. His gorgeousness is beyond that of the Orient. The eccentric and arresting words that constantly amaze the ear, bring with them a sense of things occult yet dazzling, as if we were assisting at some mystic rite, in a ritual which demanded language choice and strange.

Something of this may be due to narcotics, and to the depressing tragedy of his life. More of it is due to Shelley, Keats, and Swinburne. But these do not explain the style, nor the thoughts which clothed themselves in it. Both style and thoughts are native to the man. What he borrows he first makes his own, and thus establishes his right to borrow—a right very rarely to be conceded. Much that he has learned from Shelley he passes on to his readers, but before they receive it, it has become, not Shelley's, but Francis Thompson's. To stick a lotos-flower in our buttonhole—harris-cloth or broadcloth, it does not matter—is an impertinent folly that makes a guy of the wearer. But this man's raiment is his own, not that of other men, and Shelley himself would willingly have put his own flowers there.

Those who stumble at the prodigality and licence of his style, and the unchartered daring of his imagination, will find a most curious and brilliant discussion of the whole subject in his *Essay on Shelley*, which may be summed up in the injunction that "in poetry, as in the Kingdom of God, we should not take thought too greatly wherewith we shall be clothed, but seek first—seek *first*, not seek *only*—the spirit, and all these things will be added unto us." He discusses his own style with an unexpected frankness. His view of the use of imagination is expressed in the suggestive and extraordinary words—"To sport with the tangles of Neæra's hair may be trivial idleness or caressing tenderness, exactly as your relation to Neræa is that of heartless gallantry or of love. So you may toy with imagery in mere intellectual ingenuity, and then you might as well go write acrostics; or you may toy with it in raptures, and then you may write a *Sensitive Plant.*" If a man is passionate, and passion is choosing her own language in his work, he may be forgiven much. If he chooses strange words deliberately and in cold blood, there is no reason why we should forgive him anything.

So much has been necessary as an introduction, but our subject is neither the man Francis Thompson nor his poetry in general, but the one poem which is at once the most characteristic expression of his personality and of his poetic genius. *The Hound of Heaven* has for its idea the chase of man by the celestial huntsman. God is out after the soul, pursuing it up and down the universe. God,—but God incarnate in Jesus

Christ, whose love and death are here the embodiment and revelation of the whole ideal world. The hunted one flees, as men so constantly flee from the Highest, and seeks refuge in every possible form of earthly experience—at least in every clean and noble form, for there is nothing suggestive of low covert or the mire. It is simply the second-best as a refuge from the best that is depicted here—the earth at its pagan finest, in whose charm or homeliness the soul would fain hide itself from the spiritual pursuit. And the Great Huntsman is remorseless in his determination to win the soul for the very best of all. The soul longs for beauty, for interest, for comfort; and in the beautiful, various, comfortable life of the earth she finds them. The inner voice still tells of a nobler heritage; but she understands and loves these earthly things, and would fain linger among them, shy of the further flight.

The whole conception of the poem is the counterpart of Browning's *Easter Day*, where the soul chooses and is allowed to choose the same regions of the lesser good and beauty for its home. In that poem the soul is permitted to devote itself for ever to the finest things that earth can give—life, literature, scientific knowledge, love. The permission sends it wild with joy, and having chosen, it settles down for ever to the earth-bound life. But eternity is too long for the earth and all that is upon it. It wears time out, and all the desire of our mortality ages and grows weary. The spirit, made for immortal thoughts and loves and life, finds itself the ghastly prisoner of that which is inevitably decaying; but its immortality postpones the decent and appropriate end to an eternal mockery and doom. At last, in the tremendous close, it wakens to the unspeakable blessedness of *not* being satisfied with anything that earth can give, and so proves itself adequate for its own inheritance of immortality. In Thompson's poem the soul is never allowed, even in dream, to rest in lower things until satiety brings disillusion. The higher destiny is swift at her heels; and ever, just as she would nestle in some new covert, she is torn from it by the imperious Best of All that claims her for its own.

There is no obvious sequence of the phases of the poem, nor any logical order connecting them into a unity of experience. They may or may not be a rescript of Thompson's own inner life, but every detail might be placed in another order without the slightest loss to the meaning or the truth. The only guiding and unifying element is a purely artistic one—that of the Hound in full cry, and the unity of the poem is but that of a day's hunting. One would like to know what remote origin it is to which we owe the figure. Thompson was a Greek scholar, and some such legend as that of Actæon may well have been in his mind. But the chase of dogs was a common horror in the Middle Ages, and many of the mediæval fiends are dog-faced. In those days, when conscience had as yet received none of our modern soporifics, and men believed in hell, many a guilty sinner knew well the baying of the hell-hounds, masterless and bloody-fanged, that chased the souls of even good men up to the very gates of heaven. Conscience and remorse ran wild, and the Hound of Hell was a characteristic part of the machinery that made the tragedy of life so terrific in those old days. But here, by a *tour de force* in which is summed up the entire transformation from ancient to modern thought, the hell-hounds are transformed into the Hound of Heaven. That something or some one is out after the souls of men, no man who has understood his inner life can question for a moment. But here the great doctrine is proclaimed, that the Huntsman of the soul is Love and not Hate, eternal Good and not Evil. No matter what cries may freeze the soul with horror in the night, what echoes of the deep-voiced dogs upon the trail of memory and of conscience, it is God and not the devil that is pursuing.

The poem, by a strange device of rhythm, keeps

up the chase in the most vividly dramatic realism. The metre throughout is irregular, and the verses swing onward for the most part in long, sweeping lines. But five times, at intervals in the poem, the sweep is interrupted by a stanza of shorter lines, varied slightly but yet in essence the same—

> "But with unhurrying chase,
> And unperturbèd pace,
> Deliberate speed, majestic instancy,
> They beat—and a Voice beat
> More instant than the Feet—
> All things betray thee, who betrayest Me."

By this device of rhythm the footfall of the Hound is heard in all the pauses of the poem. In the short and staccato measures you hear the patter of the little feet padding after the soul from the unseen distance behind. It is a daring use of the onomatopœic device in poetry, and it is effective to a wonder, binding the whole poem into the unity of a single chase.

The first nine lines are the story of a soul subjective as yet and self-absorbed. The first covert in which it seeks to hide is its own life—the thoughts and tears and laughter, the hopes and fears of a man. This is in most men's lives the first attempt at escape. The verses here give the inner landscape, the country of a soul's experience, with wonderful compression. Then comes the patter of the Hound's feet, and for the rest we are no longer in the thicket of the inner life, but in the open country of the outer world. This is but the constantly repeated transition which, as we have already seen, Browning illustrates in his *Sordello*, the turning-point between the early introspective and the later dramatic periods.

Having gained the open country of the outward and objective world, the inevitable first thought is of love as a refuge from spiritual pursuit. The story is shortly told in nine lines. The human and the divine love are rivals here; pagan *versus* ideal affection. The hunted heart is not allowed to find refuge or solace in human love. The man knows that it is Love that follows him: yet it is the warm, red, earthly passion that he craves for, and the divine pursuer seems cold, exacting, and austere.

Finding no refuge in human love from this "tremendous Lover," he seeks it next in a kind of imaginative materialism, half-scientific, half-fantastic. He appeals at "the gold gateways of the stars" and at "the pale ports o' the moon" for shelter. He seeks to hide beneath the vague and blossom-woven veil of far sky-spaces, or, in lust of swift motion, "clings to the whistling mane of every wind!" Here is a choice of paganism at its most modern and most impressive. The cosmic imagination, revelling in the limitless fields of time and space, will surely be sufficient for a man's idealism, without any insistence upon further definition. Here are Carlyle's Eternities and Immensities—are they not enough? The answer is that these are but the servants of One mightier than they. Incorruptible and steadfast in their allegiance, they will neither offer pity nor will they allow peace to him who is not loyal to their Master. And the hunted soul is stung by a fever of restlessness that chases him back across "the long savannahs of the blue" to earth again, with the recurring patter of the little feet behind him.

Doubling upon the course, the quarry seeks the surest refuge to be found on earth. Children are still here, and in their simplicity and innocence there is surely a hiding-place that will suffice. Here is no danger of earthly passion, no Titanic stride among the vast things of the universe. Are they not the true idealists, the children? Are they not the authentic guardians of fairyland and of heaven? Francis Thompson is an authority here, and his love of children has expressed itself in much exqusite prose and poetry. "Know you what it is to be a child? It is to be something very different from the man of to-day. It is to have a spirit yet streaming from the waters of baptism; it is to believe in love, to believe in loveliness, to believe in belief; it is to be so little that the elves can reach to whisper in your ear; it is to turn pumpkins into coaches, and mice into horses, lowness into loftiness, and nothing into everything, for each child has its fairy godmother in its own soul; it is to live in a nutshell and to count yourself the king of infinite space." "To the last he [Shelley] was the enchanted child. . . . He is still at play, save only that his play is such as manhood stops to watch, and his playthings are those which the gods give their children. The universe is his box of toys. He dabbles his fingers in the day-fall. He is gold-dusty with tumbling amidst the stars. He makes bright mischief with the moon. The meteors nuzzle their noses in his hand. He teases into growling the kennelled thunder, and laughs at the shaking of its fiery chain. He dances in and out of the gates of heaven; its floor is littered with his broken fancies. He runs wild over the fields of ether. He chases the rolling world." He who could write thus, and who could melt our hearts with *To Monica Thought Dying* and its refrain,

> "A cup of chocolate,
> One farthing is the rate,
> You drink it through a straw, a straw, a straw"

—surely he must have had some wonderful right of entrance into the innocent fellowships of childhood.

Still more intimate, daring in its incredible humility and simpleness, is his *Ex Ore Infantium*:—

"Little Jesus, wast Thou shy
Once, and just as small as I?
And what did it feel like to be
Out of Heaven, and just like me? . . .
Hadst Thou ever any toys,
Like us little girls and boys?
And didst Thou play in Heaven with all
The angels, that were not too tall? . . .
So, a little Child, come down
And hear a child's tongue like Thy own;
Take me by the hand and walk,
And listen to my baby-talk."

But not even this refuge is open to the rebel soul.

"I turned me to them very wistfully;
But just as their young eyes grew sudden fair
With dawning answers there,
Their angel plucked them from me by the hair."

Driven from the fairyland of childhood, he flees, as a last resort, to Nature. This time it is not in science that he seeks her, but in pure abandonment of his spirit to her changing moods. He will be one with cloud and sky and sea, will be the brother of the dawn and eventide.

"I was heavy with the even,
When she lit her glimmering tapers
Round the day's dead sanctities.
I laughed in the morning's eyes,
I triumphed and I saddened with all weather."

Here again Francis Thompson is on familiar ground. If, like Mr. Chesterton, he holds the key of fairyland, like him also he can retain through life his wonder at the grass. His nature-poetry is nearer Shelley than anything that has been written since Shelley died. In it

> "The leaves dance, the leaves sing,
> The leaves dance in the breath of spring,"

or—

> "The great-vanned Angel March
> Hath trumpeted
> His clangorous 'Sleep no more' to all the dead—
> Beat his strong vans o'er earth and air and sea
> And they have heard;
> Hark to the *Jubilate* of the bird."

These, and such exquisite detailed imagery as that of the poem *To a Snowflake*—the delicate silver filigree of verse—rank him among the most privileged of the ministrants in Nature's temple, standing very close to the shrine. Yet here again there is repulse for the flying soul. This fellowship, like that of the children, is indeed fair and sheltering, but it is not for him. It is as when sunset changes the glory from the landscape into the cold and dead aspect of suddenly fallen night. Nature, that seemed so alive and welcoming, is dead to him. Her austerity and aloofness change her face; she is not friend but stranger. Her language is another tongue from his—

> "In vain my tears were wet on Heaven's grey cheek,"

—and the padding of the feet is heard again.

Thus has he compassed the length and breadth of the universe in the vain attempt to flee from God. Now at last he finds himself at bay. God has been too much for him. Against his will, and wearied out with the vain endeavour to escape, he must face the pursuing Love at last.

> "Naked I wait Thy love's uplifted stroke!
> My harness piece by piece thou hast hewn from me,
> And smitten me to my knee.
> I am defenceless utterly."

So, faced by ultimate destiny in the form of Divine Love at last, he remembers the omnipotence that once had seemed to dwell in him, when

> "In the rash lustihead of my young powers,
> I shook the pillaring hours
> And pulled my life upon me,"

and

> "The linked fantasies, in whose blossomy twist
> I swung the earth a trinket at my wrist."

All that is gone, and he is face to face with the grim demands of God.

There follows a protest against those demands. To him it appears that they are the call for sheer sacrifice and death. He had sought self-realisation in every lovely field that lay open to the earth. But now the trumpeter is sounding, "from the hid battlements of Eternity," the last word and final meaning of human life. His is a dread figure, "enwound with glooming robes purpureal, cypress-crowned." His demand is for death and sacrifice, calling the reluctant children of the green earth out from this pleasance to face the awful will of God.

It is the Cross that he has seen in nature and beyond it. Long ago it was set up in England, that same Cross, when Cynewulf sang his *Christ*. On Judgment Day he saw it set on high, streaming with blood and flame together, amber and crimson, illuminating the Day of Doom. Thompson has found it, not on Calvary only, but everywhere in nature, and by *tour de force* he blends the sunset with Golgotha and finds that the lips of Nature proclaim the Gospel of Jesus Christ. In the garden of the monastery there stands a cross, and the sun is setting over it.

"Thy straight
Long beam lies steady on the Cross. Ah me!
What secret would thy radiant finger show?
Of thy bright mastership is this the key?
Is *this* thy secret then, and is it woe?

Thou dost image, thou dost follow
That king-maker of Creation
Who ere Hellas hailed Apollo
Gave thee, angel-god, thy station;

Thou art of Him a type memorial.
Like Him thou hangst in dreadful pomp of blood
Upon thy Western rood;
And His stained brow did veil like thine to night.

Now, with wan ray that other sun of Song
Sets in the bleakening waters of my soul.
One step, and lo! the Cross stands gaunt and long
'Twixt me and yet bright skies, a presaged dole.

Even so, O Cross! thine is the victory,
Thy roots are fast within our fairest fields;
Brightness may emanate in Heaven from Thee:
Here Thy dread symbol only shadow yields."

This is ever the first appearance of the Highest when men see it. And, to the far-seeing eyes of the poet, nature must also wear the same aspect. Apollo, when his last word is said, must speak the same language as Christ. Paganism is an elaborate device to do without the Cross. Yet it is ever a futile device, for the Cross is in the very grain and essence of all life; it is absolutely necessary to all permanent and satisfying gladness. Francis Thompson is not the first who has shrunk back from the bitter truth. Many others have found the bitterness of the Cross a lesson too dreadful for their joyous or broken hearts to learn. Who are we that we should judge them? Have we not all rebelled at this bitter aspect of the Highest, and said, in our own language—

"Ah! is Thy love indeed
A weed, albeit an amaranthine weed
Suffering no flowers except its own to mount?"

Finally we have the answer of Christ to the soul He has chased down after so long a following—

"Strange, piteous, futile thing!
Wherefore should any set thee love apart?
Seeing none but I makes much of nought (He said),
And human love needs human meriting:
How hast thou merited——
Of all man's clotted clay the dingiest clot?
Alack, thou knowest not
How little worthy of any love thou art!
Whom wilt thou find to love ignoble thee,
Save Me, save only Me?
All which I took from thee I did but take,
Not for thy harms,
But just that thou mightst seek it in My arms.
All which thy child's mistake
Fancies as lost, I have stored for thee at home:
Rise, clasp my hand, and come."

And the poem ends upon the patter of the little feet—

"Halts by me that footfall:
Is my gloom, after all,
Shade of His hand, outstretched caressingly?
Ah, fondest, blindest, weakest,
I am He Whom thou seekest!
Thou drovest love from thee, who drovest Me."

It is a perfect ending for this very wonderful song of life, and it tells the old and constantly repeated story of the victory of the Cross over the pagan gods. It is through pain and not through indulgence that the ideals gain for themselves eternal life. Until the soul has been transformed and strengthened by pain, its attempt to fulfil itself and be at peace in a pagan settlement on the green earth must ever be in vain. And in our hearts we all know this quite well. We really desire the Highest, and yet we flee in terror from it always, until the day of the wise surrender. This is perhaps the greatest of all our paradoxes and contradictions.

As has been already pointed out, the new feature which is introduced to the aspect of the age-long conflict by *The Hound of Heaven* is that the parts are here reversed, and instead of the soul seeking the Highest, the Highest is out in full cry after the soul. In this the whole quest crosses over into the supernatural, and can no longer be regarded simply as a study of human nature. Beyond the human region, out among those Eternities and Immensities where Carlyle loved to roam, there is that which loves and seeks. This is the very essence of Christian faith. The Good Shepherd seeketh the lost sheep until He find it. He is found of those that sought Him not. Until the search is ended the silly sheep may flee before His footsteps in terror, even in hatred, for the bewildered hour. Yet it is He who gives all reality and beauty even to those things which we would fain choose instead of Him—He alone. The deep wisdom of the Cross knows that it is pain which gives its grand reality to love, so making it fit for Eternity, and that sacrifice is the ultimate secret of fulfilment.

Truly those who lose their life for His sake shall find it. Not to have Him is to renounce the possibility of having anything: to have Him is to have all things added unto us.

So far we have considered this poem as a record of personal experience, but it may be taken also as a message for the age in which we live. Regarded so, it is an appeal to pagan England to come back from all its idols, from its attempt to force upon the earth a worship which she repudiates:

> "Worship not me but God, the angels urge."

The angels of earth say that, as well as those of heaven—the angels of nature and the open field, of homes and the love of women and of men, of little children and of grave science and all learning. The desire of the soul is very near it, nay, is pursuing it with patient and remorseless footsteps down every quiet and familiar street. The land of heart's desire is no strange land, nor has heaven been lifted from about our heads.

> "Not where the whirling systems darken,
> And our benumbed conceiving soars!—
> The drift of pinions, would we hearken,
> Beats at our own clay-shuttered doors.
>
> The angels keep their ancient places;—
> Turn but a stone, and start a wing!
> 'Tis ye, 'tis your estrangèd faces,
> That miss the many-splendoured thing.

But (when so sad thou canst not sadder)
  Cry;—and upon thy so sore loss
Shall shine the traffic of Jacob's ladder
  Pitched between Heaven and Charing Cross.

Yea, in the night, my Soul, my daughter,
  Cry;—clinging Heaven by the hems;
And lo, Christ walking on the water,
  Not of Genesareth, but Thames."[1]

[1] These verses, probably unfinished and certainly left rough for future perfecting, were found among Francis Thompson's papers when he died.